IS NOT A

"FOUR LETTER"

WORD

CARMELA RAMAGLIA

FOOD
IS NOT A
"FOUR LETTER"
WORD

The No Diet, No Drama, No BS Way to

Create a Body AND Life You Love

Carmela Ramaglia

POWER WITHIN

Power Within Publishing
A division of Power Within Productions
Seattle, WA
Printed and Distributed by Vervante

Library of Congress Control Number: 2021901374

Paperback Edition ISBN 978-0-9828656-6-8
Digital Edition ISBN 978-0-9828656-7-5

Printed and distributed by Vervante.

Vervante
224 South Main St. #202
Springville, UT
84663

Other Works

*Happy Calories Don't Count
(neither does unhappy exercise)*

Table of Contents

(cont.)

Part Three – The Science, Spirituality and Psychology of Weight Loss

Part Four – Food for Thought: Navigating the Reality of Living in This World

Part Five – An Appetite for Life

Appendix – Hungry for More: Living in "Happy Calories World"

For Joshie

You made me do it again...

Acknowledgements

If you are familiar with my work, you know that none of this would exist without the one and only Joshua Stewart. Joshie, thank you for your constant, unwavering love and your consistent prodding, pushing me further out into the world – even when I would only go kicking and screaming. Thank you for everything you have done and continue to do – the list is endless – and for putting up with me! You deserve a parade!!! Thank you to Jo-Jo for your fabulous design work and friendship. And to Glenda, my eagle-eyed editor!! Thank you so much for your help and for reigniting my passion! Thank you to Cindy and Lindsey and the Vervante team – You Rock!! To the Happy Calories Cheerleading Team: Dana, Linda, Julie, Eli, Ayelen, Keturah and Glenda – thank you for keeping me going all these years. Any time I wondered if I was actually helping anyone at all I would always get a sweet note from one of you. And thank you to Jan and Gloria for constantly reminding me that "I'm not crazy." Thank you to Mom – there is no fiercer "Mamma Bear" around, even when you put your foot down! Thanks to Pops and Sister for keeping the fun in dysfunctional – I would not trade you for a villa in Bordighera! And the list would not be complete without the fur babies!! Giorgi, Marley and Poochie Du – you have no idea how much I love you! Finally, Kara – your letter, and Kristi – your poem, you have touched my heart in ways I could not have imagined. And to Craig. Thank you for making me a bit sad. No matter where we find ourselves in the Universe – in our next lives and the Great Beyond – I will always be your friend and I will always love you.

Preface

When I had finished writing *Happy Calories Don't Count,* I honestly thought I had said everything I needed to say on the topics of body image, personal transformation and weight loss. How could I possibly be any clearer? Happy Calories Don't Count – the statement says it all!! (Doesn't it?) At a conference a few months later, I hit it off with the girl who was checking us into the hotel. As a thank you for all of the extra courtesy and consideration, I gave her a copy of the book. A couple of nights later she hunted me down, presented me with her now dog-eared and highlighted copy and asked *"How?? How do I do this? The book is amazing – now what do I **do**?"*

"What do you mean what do you do?" I thought to myself. *"You be. And by being you know what to do."* We sat and chatted for hours that evening. It became clear that what was so obvious to me was not so obvious to everyone else. Joshie, of course, said I should write another book. Yeah...right.

Time passed and people emailed asking if I offered private coaching. More time passed and I started blogging. And made YouTube videos. I created online courses and "Booty Camps." Years later, I read *Happy Calories Don't Count* as if for the first time. *"It's all in there,"* I thought. *"What am I missing?"*

I was missing the fact that I had developed an "unconscious competence" over the course of my own painful and life-threatening saga with my body and my weight. I could see and accept simple truths because I had lived them. The challenge I was now facing was how to help others "see the light" so to speak without their having to go to those deep, dark places.

Once again, Joshie said to write another book. Once again, I politely ignored him. One day Joshie handed me a document outlining the guidelines for submitting a book proposal to a major literary agent. I looked at the submission requirements and knew the answers to every question. Apparently, I had already written a book in my head!

So here it is. *Food Is Not a Four-Letter Word: The No Diet, No Drama, No BS Way to Create a Body AND Life You Love.* It is the "how to" book. It is the answer to my friend's questions from oh so long ago – how "to do" *Happy Calories Don't Count.* This book outlines my 5-step method – the "doing" part. It also discusses the "being" part – how to live, survive and thrive in the mass media, marketing culture in which we live. This book includes an appendix of Frequently Asked Questions and offers a chapter of "Carmela-isms" when you need a quick boost of inspiration on your journey.

Now I truly have said everything I have to say on the topics of personal transformation, body image, self-esteem and weight loss. Until Joshie tells me to write another book. Yeah...right.

Editorial Note

"You write like you speak!" This is what people seem to appreciate the most. I have often heard my readers say that they feel like I am just having a conversation with them over a cup of coffee. And is the intent. How else would I even be able to approach such personal and painful subjects such as body image and weight? The problem is that my writing style could leave my former English professors pulling their hair out. (See? I just ended a sentence with a preposition...) I could argue that the rules have already been broken by text lingo and Twitter. But that doesn't address the issues of interweaving sentence subjects (i.e., sometimes writing "you" as the subject and sometimes writing "we" as the subject). So, let me just hash that out for you right here. I am writing to you – the reader – about how to heal your pain, shame and drama around your body and your weight. (I assume you are dealing with such issues because you picked up this book in the first place.) In this book, I am teaching you how to find peace and freedom with food and exercise. I am teaching you how to create a body and life you love. But you are not alone! I have dealt with this stuff too (that's why I write about it). And we are not alone. Unofficial surveys claim that most women in industrialized nations suffer from weight and body drama. So, as I write, sometimes I will use "you" as the subject. Sometimes I use "we." And sometimes they might even alternate! I don't censor myself in such manners when I speak from the heart and I don't censor myself when writing from the heart either.

Part One

An Introduction

Our greatest strengths come from our deepest wounds.

~ Unknown

Chapter 1

My Superpower

"If you could have one superpower what would it be?" I don't know if anyone asks this question anymore, but it used to be a common icebreaker. While other people would offer up such exciting powers as flying, teleporting, or being invisible, I would always say I wanted to be able to heal people. I would offer up healing abilities as a superpower because I was too ashamed to admit the one power that I truly, desperately wanted: to be able to eat whatever I wanted whenever I wanted without having to worry about getting fat – to have food just be a non-issue and still look good. I bet that confession just opened up a big can of worms. Some may see this as vanity. Some may bristle at the word "fat." Some people (who probably aren't reading this book) may think all of this is silly and a waste of time. But I promise you it is not. Your body is the vehicle through which you experience this life. Period. It does not matter if you are coming at things from a general health and fitness perspective, a deeper emotional and spiritual point of view, or a body image/body positivity frame of mind. If your experience of your body is not happy, neither is your life experience. It simply cannot be.

How you feel *in* your body and *about* your body is a very big deal. It influences *everything* – your sense of self, your relationships, your career, your finances, your health – everything. How you feel in and about your body literally affects the quality of your life.

If you picked up this book, the quality of your life is likely compromised. And you are not alone. With the amount of time, money and energy – physical, mental, emotional, and spiritual energy – most women often spend dealing with body anxiety, shame and hatred, we are prevented from truly living. Furthermore, our families, friends and society as a whole lose out on the unique gifts that only we can offer.

This book is about optimizing your quality of life. You won't learn what to eat to "master your metabolism," how to train so that you can "keep burning fat hours after your workout," or the "secret to manifesting" your dream body. This is not a self-help or personal development book that motivates you to "embrace your inner goddess" and "overcome those obstacles" that are keeping you from your diet, fitness and weight loss goals. Rather this book offers an honest and intelligent conversation on personal transformation, specifically in the areas of body image and weight loss. This book discusses everything from the physical to the metaphysical, from body shame to body positivity, through a very specific lens – the lens of my own hard-fought experience. For through that experience I have developed my coveted superpower. I really can eat whatever I want whenever I want and not have to worry about getting fat. Food truly is a non-issue and I do feel good in my body and about my body. And now I realize that my answer to that icebreaker question was not actually wrong – I do want to heal people – and I can. If you deal with diet drama - stress, anxiety, frustration, pain or shame around food, exercise, your body or your weight – the principles outlined in this book will heal you. You will discover a sense of peace, freedom and joy that you didn't know was possible. You will learn how to optimize your health, vitality and wellbeing. You will finally be able to create a body *and* a life you love.

Chapter 2

The Lettuce Burrito

I blew my very first professional acting audition because I could not bring myself to take a bite out of a lettuce burrito. You heard me. I could not take a bite out of a burrito shell filled with *lettuce.* I did not know how many calories were in a bite of a lettuce burrito. And if I did not know how many calories I would have consumed, I would not know how many extra minutes I would have to spend on the treadmill to burn them off.

I know that might sound a little crazy to you. Or maybe you can relate. Or perhaps you have a Spidey Sense going off in your head shouting, "Eating Disorder

Alert!" If that is the case, you aren't too far off base. But this book is not about eating disorders. Yes, I have had my fair share of experience. At seventeen I was hospitalized for anorexia at eighty pounds. By twenty-five, I had been in treatment four more times. And at thirty, I was somehow two hundred pounds – and suicidal. But this is not about me. This is about *you*. You see the thing that makes eating disorders so difficult to overcome – to truly put to bed – is the *exact same thing* that keeps you stuck in your pain and your shame around your body and your weight if you are one of the *ninety-one per cent*[1] of women who feel bad about their bodies. And it is the exact same thing that will put unnecessary, artificial limits on your health, vitality, wellbeing and joy if you don't happen to suffer from body image issues.

To help you understand my perspective, I would like you to consider an alternative audition scenario. If I had been a recovering alcoholic and the casting director had handed me a bottle of beer to drink for my audition, would that have been different? If so, why? This is important because pop culture psychology – and much

---

1   *Surveys done by the Body Image Movement show that 91-93% of women hate their bodies.*

of the medical community – places eating disorders in the same general category as alcoholism and drug addiction. This is because the basic pathology for all three conditions is generally viewed as essentially the same – simply a maladaptive coping mechanism masking some deeper underlying psychological and/or emotional issue.

Because of this, the treatment for all three conditions follows the same general, basic protocol:

1. Put the patient in a facility where they cannot engage in their maladaptive behavior.

2. Send the patient to therapy so they can start to explore some of these deeper underlying issues – the childhood trauma, the dysfunctional family of origin, etc.

3. Provide the patient with new skill sets and tools they can use to deal with Life's challenges (instead of their maladaptive coping device).

4. Provide the patient with a network of support resources so that once they leave treatment, they can go on to be functional, engaged, happy human beings. (At least that's the theory, right?)

Well, there are two really big problems with treating eating disorders this way. The first one is kind of obvious if you stop and think about it... *You can't **not** eat!* You can go through alcohol or drug rehab and then go on to live a happy, engaged, meaningful life without ever touching another drug or drop of alcohol again. That is possible. But you can't not eat – *you have to deal with the food.* Which brings us to the second problem with treating eating disorders like drug or alcohol addiction. Do you know how eating disorder treatment centers keep their patients from engaging in their maladaptive coping mechanisms while they are working out their mommy issues and their daddy issues? They put you on a *diet.* Yep – you heard me. *They put you on a **diet***! Granted, it could be a "high calorie diet" if you are anorexic. Or it could be a "structured meal plan" if you happen to suffer from bulimia or compulsive overeating (a.k.a binge eating). But it doesn't matter what fancy, euphemistic label they put on it. At the end of the day, it is still a diet. And that, my friend, is the rub. That is the Catch-22 that keeps everyone – even if you don't suffer from an "eating disorder" – stuck. They constantly tell you, "It's not about the food." But when it comes to your physical body, they *make* it about the food.

Therefore, it really does not matter how much therapy you have had. It does not matter how much personal development or spiritual growth you have gone through. It does not matter how enlightened you become, how emotionally savvy or spiritually sophisticated you are. When you get right down to it, everyone ultimately boils your physical body down to a *balance sheet of transactions* between what food goes in and what exercise burns it off.

Now we all deal with this "diet and exercise" dilemma in our own unique ways. Some people nitpick the food. Some people nitpick the exercise. And some people journey down the paths of personal growth and spirituality - and may not even remember or realize that this food in/exercise out balance sheet was the core problem they were trying to solve in the first place. It does not matter what approach we take. The bottom line is that on some level, *we all fundamentally believe that we have to pay a price to eat.* The price? Exercise – or weight gain.

So I ask you: Am I still crazy for blowing my

audition? Of course I was crazy for blowing my audition! It was *lettuce!* It was a *bite!* But what if it wasn't lettuce? What if it was pizza? Or ice cream? And what if it wasn't a bite? What if – sixty-eight takes later – it ended up being an entire pizza? Or a pint of ice cream? Where's the line??

Let me share a hard-discovered Truth with you: *there is no line.* There is no line because it is not about the food. It turns out that "they" are actually on the right track. "They" are *partially* right! It isn't about the food. What "they" need to learn is that it is not about the food when it comes to your physical body either. Apples, Twinkies, it is all the same. Now, before you get all excited and start writing nasty letters to my publisher and attacking me on Twitter because you think I just said that a Twinkie is as good as an apple – I did not. I said the Twinkie is the *same* as the apple. The Twinkie is the *same* as the apple because *it isn't about either.* It is not about the food – whatever the food is.

"It" is about your body. Your body is a complex system of Living Intelligence that is seeking at each and every moment to optimize itself. Your body can heal itself of wounds! Your body can overcome illness! Your body can even create and sustain Life itself! Your body knows how to create an optimized state of health, vitality, wellbeing, beauty and joy. Your body *knows what it needs* to create this optimal condition and it is *communicating this information to you all the time.* This is important so I'll say it again: Your body knows what it needs to create this optimal condition and it is communicating this information to you all the time.

Unfortunately, there is often a breakdown in communication. And this breakdown is generally on your end. You will never be able to truly hear – or trust – the wisdom of your body if you are listening to all of those cultural messages that are constantly drilled into and running through your head.

We live in a culture that suggests that we can – and should – control our body and our weight by controlling what we eat and what we do for exercise. We live in a culture that suggests that if we are not the size, shape or weight we want to be, we are at best unmotivated or undisciplined or at worst, we are lazy or stupid. Because everyone "knows" what to do to lose weight and get in shape, right? It's diet and exercise. (And if, for some strange reason "diet and exercise" does not work, then "there is something wrong with your metabolism.")

But the fact that we are *responsible* for what we eat – and *responsible* for what we do for exercise – **does not** mean that we can therefore *control our body and our weight through diet and exercise.* That is a fallacy! That is **the** fallacy upon which the entire diet, fitness and weight loss industries base their business models. That is the fallacy by which the publishing industry sells its women's magazines. And that is the fallacy that lies at the root of your pain and shame around your body.

Now one of two things is probably going on about now. Either this is the most exciting and liberating thing you have ever heard and you're thinking, "Wow! It's not my fault! I'm not bad or wrong or stupid or lazy. This is incredible!!" Or this is the most terrifying thing you have ever heard and you want to stop reading this book. Please don't. I *get* it. If you had told me way back when that I could not control my body, I would have thought you were just jealous and trying to trick me. After all, even the "expert" doctors in the hospital were controlling my body with their high calorie diets and bed rest. And I would have been angry with you. You would have been striking the nerve of my deepest fear.

If I couldn't control my body, how would I know I would be ok? How would I know how to be a woman? How would I know how to fit into society? How would I live?

Fortunately, there are other industries besides diet, fitness and weight loss where we can look for guidance. And in every other one of these industries, we recognize the value and importance of these things called *relationships*. We understand the vital role relationships play in driving outcomes and creating success. We understand that the best salespeople engage their clients and customers in relationships. The best leaders and managers build strong teams through cultivating relationships. From manufacturing to customer service, we understand the crucial role relationships play in creating the outcomes we desire. But no one ever thinks about creating an honest-to-goodness relationship with our bodies. Wouldn't that make sense? That creating a relationship (that thing that is so crucial to creating success) with our body (that thing that knows how to create an optimized state of health, vitality and wellbeing) would be an important thing to do?

When we take the time – and make the effort – to switch from a transaction-based model of "diet and exercise" (where calories are a "currency of exchange"), to a relationship-based model of health and wellbeing, our entire experience of our body changes. We recognize that our weight is neither our fault, nor to our credit. That monkey is finally off our backs!! It is replaced by a feeling of deep peace and freedom. When we switch from a transaction-based model of "diet and exercise" to a relationship-based model, our entire experience of food and exercise also changes. We suddenly stop judging our food – it is no longer "good" or "bad." Food is not a four-letter word – it no longer comes with a "cost." Exercise is no longer a penalty or a punishment for it is not the "price you have to pay to eat." All of the stress and pain, drama and dysfunction around food and exercise are healed. We are free! When we switch from a transaction-based model to a relationship-based model, we have the space and grace to listen to our bodies. And we start to respect our bodies. In a relationship-based model we can become *embodied*. And when we are embodied, we instinctively make choices that contribute to our greatest health, wellbeing and joy. If this sounds good to you, keep reading. The next section will explain how to do all of this with the 5

Steps of the Happy Calories Don't Count® Method. You will learn how to create a body *and* a life you love.

Part Two

End the Food Fight

*The
Happy Calories Don't Count®
Method*

You never change things by fighting the existing reality. To change something, build a new model that makes the existing model obsolete.

~ Buckminster Fuller

Chapter 3

Step One

Embrace a Model of Alignment

Ok, what does *that* mean? It means stop thinking in terms of "diet and exercise!" Yes, what you eat is important. And moving your body is important. But food and exercise are *not* important in the way we have been taught. We have been taught that our bodies are essentially a caloric balance sheet - that what we eat and what we do for exercise directly impacts our weight and shape. Eat more, eat high carbs, eat high fat, eat sugar, eat fill-in-the blank, and we will gain weight. Eat less, eat vegetables, eat low glycemic, eat lean protein, eat fill-in-the blank and we will lose weight. Exercise more, lose weight. Stop exercising, gain weight. To embrace a Model of Alignment means to give all of that up. To embrace a Model of Alignment means to stop looking at food and exercise in terms of how they will affect your body. It means stop making food choices based on how much you think it will "cost you" in terms of exercise, weight-gain, or health "benefits" or "consequences." It means stop looking at the calorie content on the food labels. It means stop looking at the caloric displays on the cardio machines. It means to let food be food and exercise be exercise. And I know that can be hard to do in the beginning.

Our entire culture is built around this transaction-based "diet and exercise" idea. We live in a mass media marketing driven society that uses this "diet and exercise" mindset as the underlying base argument to sell products and services. Have you ever seen or heard things like this?

This dessert only has 100 calories!

This supplement burns calories and fat while you sleep!

*We know getting in shape is hard – that's why
our personal trainers keep you motivated
during your calorie-busting workouts!*

We also use this "diet and exercise" model as part of superficial everyday chitchat. We talk about sports, the weather and our diets – "I shouldn't eat this – oh well, I'll just burn it off later." Nature abhors a vacuum – and so do our minds. Therefore, it is nearly impossible to let the "diet and exercise" model go without something with which your mind can replace it. And if you cannot exorcise "diet and exercise" from your mind, you will always be limited in your results – and your joy.

***The Model of Alignment is the replacement
for the "diet and exercise" idea.
It fills that void. It is the first step.***

Now, what exactly is this model? "Alignment" means a lot of different things to a lot of different people. The corporate world wants to align their visions with their values and metaphysicians want to align their vibrations with Source Energy. So, what do I mean when I say "Alignment?" Here's a picture:

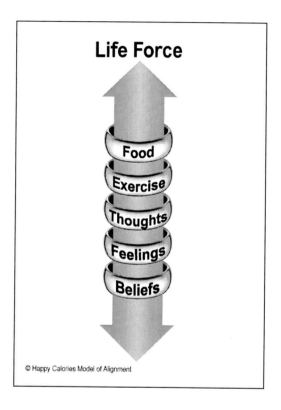

Look at the picture and hear this. Alignment is a *literal metaphor*. This is important so I'll say it again: *Alignment is a literal metaphor.*

To help you understand it, let me tell you about my inspiration for this idea. First off, in addition to many other things, I am a classically trained, certified Pilates instructor. I built my first studio in 2004 and have spent years observing and correcting my clients' physical alignment.

Physical alignment is a very interesting thing. When your shoulders are square over your hips – and your hips are square over your knees – and knees over toes – and you are recruiting the correct muscles to perform the given activity – your body – as a physical system – works efficiently and effectively. Energy levels increase, aches and pains disappear, and your body expresses the natural joy of being alive with freedom, grace and ease.

But you are not just a physical system (as that "diet and exercise" model suggests). You are also an emotional system, an intellectual system, and a spiritual system. And these parts of you also need to be addressed. So I envisioned a metaphor that embraced the totality of who you are as a human being. And what is great is that this metaphor is valid, regardless of your personal belief system!

Look at that illustration again. Each of the rings represents an aspect of what you are as a human being. Since we are specifically addressing food, body and weight issues, I have rings dedicated to our food, exercise, thoughts, feelings and beliefs. But this model would also work for other areas of our lives. Instead of having individual rings for food and exercise, we can simply have one ring representing actions.

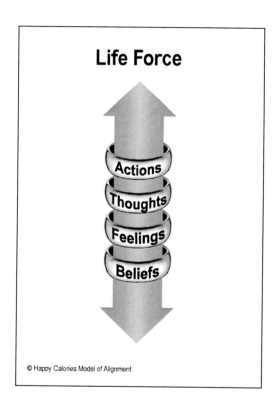

© Happy Calories Model of Alignment

There is also an arrow. This arrow represents the energy of Life Force. So depending on your point of view this could be God, Source Energy, or simply the bioelectrical impulses that animate the human body. It does not matter what you believe about the nature of the universe. In this model, the arrow is energy – energy running through a system – and that system is You.

When these rings – representing the totality of who you are – are aligned, that arrow of energy can move through the integrated system that is You powerfully and effectively. When the rings are misaligned, the energy cannot move powerfully or effectively – if it can flow at all. (There is an illustration of this concept on the following page.)

This model is a literal metaphor because I am talking about the literal alignment – the congruency – of the elements that make us human. It is a metaphor because you aren't really a picture of five gold rings stacked on top of each other. You are a real live person.

Now here is a very important point to note. *Pay attention.* In the "diet and exercise" model, the assumption is that any change in your body is coming from some sort of action or work you are doing with respect to diet and/or exercise.

But in the Alignment Model, the change in your body is coming from the *energy flowing through the system.* The change in your body is coming from the *flow of Life Energy* – not from any *specific work* you are doing regarding the *details* of your food or exercise. The change is coming from the energy of Life Force flowing through you. (Maybe *this* is that mysterious thing called metabolism.)

In the Alignment Model, the "work" is about getting your metaphorical rings into literal alignment so that the energy of Life can run powerfully and effectively through you on your behalf. Your work is about getting your thoughts, feelings, beliefs and actions about food and exercise into harmony. Your work is about becoming congruent with yourself. And when you are congruent with yourself – when your thoughts, feelings, beliefs and actions are aligned – you are at peace with yourself. You are happy.

I will say this again. Food and exercise are important. But they are not important like you have been taught. Your thoughts, feelings and beliefs matter. Let's use this Model of Alignment in an example.

Suppose you are at a restaurant and you think, "I should have a salad." And you feel, "Yeah, a salad sounds good!" And you believe, "Yes! I need my veggies today." If you order a salad and eat it, your thoughts, feelings, beliefs and actions are congruent. Your metaphorical rings are in literal alignment and Life Force can flow powerfully through the system that is you, and that salad will serve you.

If, however, you are at a restaurant and you think, "I really want this pasta dish, but it's full of carbs. So I guess I'll settle for a salad." And you feel, *"Salad?? Really?? I hate* being on this stupid diet – I want the pasta!" And you believe, "No one ever got thin eating pasta – you have to count your calories and mind your carbs. Well, except maybe cousin Betsy – I *hate* her – she has such a fast metabolism she can eat anything she wants." And you order the salad and eat it – but it doesn't satisfy you physically, emotionally, mentally or spiritually – your metaphorical rings are out of literal alignment. Visually speaking, you are pulling those rings in the illustration off center and in opposition to each other.

Life Force

© Happy Calories Model of Alignment

You feel upset, you feel depressed, you feel deprived and (even worse!) that salad does not ultimately serve you.

Again, this is the important point to remember. The change in your body is coming from the *energy flowing through your aligned system* – **not** from the specifics of your food or exercise choices. So if you are eating a salad – but you are out of Alignment with the action – Life energy cannot flow through the system very well and that salad will do nothing to help you achieve your goals. And given the above scenario, the pasta dish is also out of Alignment and would do nothing to help you achieve your goals. But since weight-loss is so often viewed through the perspective of the "diet and exercise" model, the failure to achieve your goals would be attributed to the high carb pasta dish. Or if you did indeed choose the salad – to some defect in your metabolism. But in reality, the problem is the misalignment of the system. You are out of harmony with yourself. You are anxious and stressed out.

To correct the issue, you need to find congruency among your thoughts, feelings, beliefs and actions. (Illustration on the next page.)

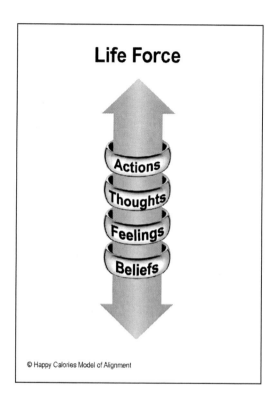

© Happy Calories Model of Alignment

Then you will find some peace. Life Energy can flow through you and it would not matter what dish you choose.

And the great thing about this model is that it is relative. Any and all of these metaphorical rings can shift in relation to the others to align with one another. So this model allows for growth. It allows for change.

Let's take another example – that dreaded office birthday party. Someone at work is having a birthday and the office social committee bought a huge cake to celebrate. But you are on a diet. (Or don't eat sugar or carbs or gluten as part of your "lifestyle.") But everyone is taking a break to have some fun in the lunchroom and eat cake. And you want to be social. And you do *like* cake. But you are watching your carbs. This is another example of being at odds with yourself. Your thoughts are in opposition to your feelings are in opposition to your beliefs. When you are out of Alignment, it does not matter if you eat the cake or not – neither action will benefit you. Eating the cake will not serve you. And not eating the cake will lead to the experience of "I just look at a piece of cake and I gain weight!" This issue is not the action. The issue is not the food. The issue is not whether you eat the food or not. The issue is your State of Being. The issue is being in Alignment with yourself.

So how do you get into Alignment? This is where the work of personal growth and spiritual principles come into play. This is where you can choose to look at situations from another perspective. This where you can explore some of your thoughts and beliefs. Remember, the action (eating the cake or not eating the cake) is irrelevant.

The goal is to harmonize your thoughts, feelings and beliefs to be congruent with the action regarding the cake. Here's a Hot Tip: It is *a lot easier* to come into Alignment around the action that already has the strongest emotional and psychological pull.

For example, if you *really* think cake – with all of its "empty calories" and sugar and carbs – is bad for you, and you just *know* you would feel guilty and try to skip dinner and spend another hour on the treadmill later, those are some pretty strong thoughts and feelings. And if those feelings are stronger than any sense of feeling "left out" of the office party, then it would be easier to come into Alignment around the idea of not eating the cake. But if you have had enough life experience and read enough books and no longer truly think that eating a piece of cake would really harm you – especially if it would help you bond with your colleagues – then it would be easier to Align with the idea of eating the cake.

As they[2] say, "If you're going to worry, don't

---

2   Quote attributed to various authors, including Don Ward and
      Michael Nolan.

~ 35 ~

do it. If you do it, don't worry." But don't worry. If you are not going to eat the cake today, that does not mean you won't ever be able to eat cake. Thoughts, feelings and beliefs can change! That is the beauty of Life! (And that is the beauty of this Alignment Model!) You can actively change your thoughts, feelings and beliefs through the work of personal and spiritual growth – or they can passively change with life experience. And when the day comes that you can be in Alignment with yourself about eating that piece of cake at the office birthday party, enjoy the heck out of it!

Now it is important to remember that Alignment is a *model* - it is a way of illustrating a concept and expressing an idea. If you have suffered with weight and body drama for a while and have wandered down the road of metaphysics, it can be very tempting to think, "Oh, I just get into Alignment and then I get the body that I want." But that is another mind trap. This is not magic. And we will discuss all this from a Law of Attraction perspective later.

For now, understand that the beauty of the Alignment Model is the shift in responsibility and ownership.

Because *you* are not responsible for the outcome – Life Force flowing through you is responsible for the outcome – you are freed of any shame, pain or guilt you may feel about your body. Furthermore, this model – this way of illustrating a concept – is a vital step in being able to free yourself from "diet and exercise" thinking. Remember, you must *exorcise* "diet and exercise" thinking from your mind. You must do this so that you can truly hear the impulses coming from your body. Your body is the key! It knows how to create the results you seek.

Alignment is a critical step. But it is not the only step. There are 5 steps in the Happy Calories Don't Count® method. Let's move on to the next one.

Chapter 4

Step Two

Connect With Your Body

If someone put a gun to my head and said that I had to reduce the Happy Calories Don't Count® method down to a single step, it would be this one: Connect With Your Body. Which begs the question, "Why Carmela? Why – if connecting with your body is so important – is it not Step 1?"

Well, it is actually a pretty easy answer. I created Happy Calories® for me – to help me overcome the stress and anxiety of diet and exercise drama – and for all of you out there like me. And if you had told me oh so long ago that the way to create a body I loved – a body that I felt good in and a body that I felt good about – was to connect with it, I would have turned and run as fast and as far away from you as I could get. Why? Because if I were to connect with my body, I might *feel* my body. And if I *felt* my body, I would feel the *pain*. I would feel the pain of being on a diet all the time. I would feel the pain of being hungry. I would feel the pain of eating food (when I did eat) that I didn't really like. I would feel the pain of beating my body up at the gym every day. And if I felt the pain of all of that, I might not be able to continue to do it. I might not be able to continue to do the things society was telling me I needed to do to get the body that I wanted.

The "diet and exercise" model demands that we disconnect from our bodies to be "successful." We can't eat when we are hungry. We can't eat what we "feel like eating." We can only eat when and what the diet – that external source – tells us to eat. The same is true for exercise. We can't just move our bodies simply to express the joy of being alive in a physical body. We have to "burn those calories, build that muscle, get into that zone, remember our goals, overcome those obstacles (our body) and maintain that mindset of success!"

And while "listen to your body" is a common sound bite these days, it is impossible to truly listen to (or trust) your body if you are operating from within the context of the "diet and exercise" model. And as I mentioned in the last chapter, your mind abhors a vacuum. So without something else – a Model of Alignment – to use as your frame of reference, you will just go back to thinking in terms of "diet and exercise."

So we *need* Step 1: Embrace a Model of Alignment, to get to Step 2: Connect With Your Body and to all the other steps that follow. And the interesting thing is, once all of that "diet and exercise" junk is finally out of your head, connecting with your body is a very natural and easy thing to do. It happens organically because you now have the mental, emotional and spiritual space for it.

So now take a deep breath. Go ahead. Take a deep breath. What did that feel like? Did you breathe in through your nose, your mouth, or both? Did you breathe all the way down into your lower abdomen? Or did you stop at your neck? *How* did you breathe? What did it *feel* like? There are no right or wrong answers. This is just an exercise to explore your body – and to see how aware of it you might (or might not) be. How is your posture as you read this book? Is your head down and forward, compressing your neck as you read these words? Are your shoulders rounded forward? Where is your center of gravity? How does it *feel* to be in your body?

Now – is there anything that you would like to change? Do you have an impulse to do something – to sit up or wiggle or breathe again? Whatever your impulse is, follow it. Where did that lead you? What does your body feel like now? What does it feel like to be in your body? Do you have another impulse? Follow it. Where does it lead?

I know this may seem like a lot. You might even be thinking, "How am I supposed to get anything done if I have to keep stopping to pay attention to my body?" Don't worry. With practice this will become second nature. Fully inhabiting your body will become a sixth sense. So it is important that you take the time to practice.

Unlike the transaction-based model of "diet and exercise," Happy Calories Don't Count® is a relationship-based approach – the primary relationship, of course, being between you and your body. And great relationships are built through respect, communication, and putting in the time to get to know one another.

Speaking of great relationships, it is time to address one of my pet peeves – those ubiquitous Fitbits, Apple Watches and other "health and fitness" trackers. Everywhere I turn people are talking about how many steps they have taken, calories they have burned, or they are entering their food into their device. Now my issue is not with these gadgets themselves. In fact, I use a similar tool in my own life. (You can read all about my little Hello Kitty notebooks in my first book, *Happy Calories Don't Count.*) My issue lies with the fact that, by their very nature, these devices will keep you stuck in the "diet and exercise" model. By focusing on the data, you miss all the other ways in which your body tries to communicate with you. By focusing on data that is generated by some outside technological gizmo instead of choosing your actions based on the information your body itself is trying to communicate to you, you can inadvertently undermine the most important relationship you have – the relationship with your body.

To me, the Fitbits, Apple Watches, fitness trackers, etc. – and all the other latest and greatest electronic gizmos leveraging the latest technology – are some of the best examples to illustrate this paradigm shift we need to create. Technology keeps evolving quickly, but our health and wellness worldview remains the same. Entrepreneurs keep trying to find applications for "visionary" and "innovative" new technology in the weight loss arena. But they are still using that same, outdated "diet and exercise" model.

Instead of using next-gen technology to reinforce the "diet and exercise" model, can we use it to enhance the relationship with our body? Perhaps – but we would first have to change the economic infrastructure of the culture. And that is a tall order. So, let's keep it simple. Breathe and connect with your body.

Chapter 5

Step Three

Enjoy Your Food

Step 3 is a short, simple and fun one. I give you full permission to enjoy your food! After all, if you stop and think about it, why wouldn't you enjoy your food?

You wouldn't enjoy your food if it were something distasteful to you but you were eating it anyway because of some diet. Well, there are no diets in "Happy Calories World!"

You also would not enjoy your food if you believed you would feel guilty for eating it and thought you would have to "pay" for it later. Again, this is old "diet and exercise" thinking. Happy Calories Don't "Count" because *there is no price to pay to eat!*

This is a relationship-based model and the relationship is **not** between diet and exercise. There is *no* relationship between diet and exercise! *The relationship is between you and your body.* This is extremely important, so I'll say it again. There is *no* relationship between diet and exercise! *The relationship is between you and your body.*

Food is not "good" or "bad." Food is not a four-letter word!! Food is simply a vehicle through which you express yourself in relationship to your body. And that's why Step 2: Connect with Your Body comes before Step 3: Enjoy Your Food.

Connect with your body. Breathe deeply and feel your body. Ask your body what it wants and needs – it will tell you. And when you are inspired to eat something, enjoy it to the fullest.

Chapter 6

Step Four

Exercise Daily to Connect With and Tune Your Body

Now don't freak out about this exercise business. Let's walk back through those first few steps and you will come to understand the brilliance of this approach. Step 1 (Embrace a Model of Alignment) is all about breaking free of that "diet and exercise" mindset. Then, you have the space and grace to Connect With Your Body (Step 2). When you are connected with your body, you can trust its impulses and Enjoy Your Food (Step 3). Because you are not thinking in terms of "diet and exercise," you are connected to your body and you are enjoying your food without fear of retribution, you no longer have any resistance or resentment toward exercise!

Exercise is not a penalty. It is not a punishment. It is not the "price you pay to eat!" Notice that the phrasing of Step 4 is actually pretty long. Exercise Daily to Connect With and Tune Your Body. Why are you exercising? To connect with and tune your body! Let's practice that again. Why are you exercising?? To connect with and tune your body!!

Exercise has absolutely nothing at all to do with burning calories or losing weight! I know – it sounds crazy. So let me say it again. Exercise has absolutely nothing at all to do with burning calories or losing weight! Once you start thinking that, you are back in "Diet Drama Land."

Yes, our bodies *need* to move. But "burning calories" and "losing weight" are not the reasons why. We are physical beings living in a physical world and our bodies need to move to express that physicality. It is just like walking your dog. Does your dog really care what size it is? Of course not! But it still wants (and needs) to go for a walk every day. Exercise has nothing to do with burning calories or losing weight *and* it is a vital part of the physical experience.

Moreover, in the context of relationship, exercise is like a date with your body. Exercise is where you get to spend dedicated quality time getting to know your body. Exercise is where you learn to feel what it feels like when your heart rate goes up – and to feel what it feels like when your heart rate comes back down. Exercise is where you learn what it feels like to work a muscle and to stretch a muscle. Exercise is where you practice learning what it feels like to be *in* your body. Exercise is how you learn to become *embodied*. And the best part is, once you are embodied you will *know* what to eat, how much to eat and when.

So what exercise is best? Whatever you enjoy. Remember this is not a transaction-based model of "diet and exercise." This is a relationship-based model of Alignment. Your thoughts, feelings, and beliefs matter. That is why you experience that mysterious plateau (or get injured) in your training as soon as you start to become bored or disenchanted with your workout routines. That is why you can begrudgingly workout like a beast at the gym every day but fail to see any breathtaking results. The results do not come from the specifics of the exercise routine. The results come from the energy of Life Force flowing powerfully through you when you are in harmony and congruent with yourself about the given fitness activity.

So, from an Alignment perspective, the best exercise for you is one that you think, feel and believe good things about and makes you happy. And from the perspective of the 5 Step Happy Calories Don't Count® Method, the best exercise for you is one that you think, feel and believe good things about, makes you happy, *and* helps you cultivate that relationship with your body.

From a Happy Calories® "5 Step" perspective, those people on the cardio machines watching the TV monitors or reading the tabloid magazines really are not maximizing the potential of their workout time. Sure, they might be in Alignment with it. They may think, feel and believe that cardio is good for them. And they might not mind doing it because they can be "entertained." But they are missing out on the greatest potential of exercise – to connect with and deepen the relationship with their body.

So exercise – consciously – in ways you enjoy – daily. Your body will thank you.

Chapter 7

Step Five

Clear the Channel

Step 5 is where you get to put all of your personal growth, spirituality and self-help skills to the test. The phrase "Clear the Channel" refers to that literal metaphor of Alignment – those rings (representing the totality of who we are as human beings) and that arrow of energy (representing Life Force).

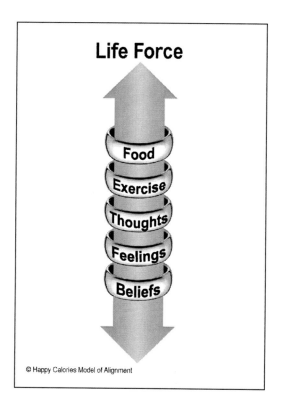

© Happy Calories Model of Alignment

When your metaphorical rings are literally aligned, the energy of Life Force can move through you powerfully and effectively. Not only can this flow of Life Force create miracles, it brings feelings of peace and harmony. When your metaphorical rings are literally aligned, you are reconciled. You are in harmony with yourself and you are happy.

But there is this thing called Life. Life happens. It throws us curve balls. It gives us challenges. And when we are challenged, our "channel" of rings can get knocked out of whack or clogged with negativity. So Step 5 is about using our personal development skills to re-harmonize ourselves and clear that negativity.

This step also probably best illustrates the radically unique and evolutionary nature of the Happy Calories Don't Count® Method. When coming from a "diet and exercise" perspective, most people do the work of personal and spiritual development to help them find success *within* the "diet and exercise" model.

For example, someone might go to therapy to heal their intimacy, inner child, fill-in-the-blank issues because pop culture psychology suggests that when these issues are "healed," this person would no longer want to "seek comfort" in food. For this food comes at a cost and eating for "emotional" reasons would negatively impact that caloric balance sheet. So if this person healed the underlying emotional problem, they would be able to successfully stay on their diet. Or someone might go to a self-help workshop to overcome their self-esteem issues so that they can believe they are "worth it" and will therefore have the internal motivation to do the work of a fitness program to get in shape. Or someone might go to a retreat to "discover the goddess within" so they can learn the secret of manifesting their ideal body without having to diet or exercise.

But what if someone didn't have any food, weight or body image issues at all? What do people who don't struggle with these issues go to therapy or self-help seminars for? Relationships!

We do all of this work on ourselves to *improve our relationships!* We heal our dramas and traumas and discover our authentic selves in order to improve our relationships - our relationship with our self, our relationships with others, our relationship with money, or our relationship with the Universe. We do all of this work to learn skills to address, understand and express our emotions in productive ways so that they do not negatively impact our relationships. We learn communication skills to deepen and improve our relationships.

So, in this relationship-based model of Happy Calories Don't Count®, we use all of the self-help and personal development skills in our toolkits to help us deal with Life's challenges in a way that does not negatively impact the *relationship* we have with our body. Clearing the Channel is not about learning how to not eat a cookie when you are sad, mad or lonely. Clearing the Channel is about learning how to deal with Life in a way that does not interfere with your relationship with your body. It is akin to not taking the frustration of the day's work out on your family during dinner.

Deal with your upsets, so that you can enjoy your relationships. Clear that Channel so that Life Force can once again move freely and powerfully through you – creating magnificent things on your behalf.

There you have it – the Happy Calories Don't Count® Method – five simple steps for healing all of the stress and anxiety about food, exercise, your body and your weight. Five simple steps for creating a body and a life you love.

Step 1) Embrace a Model of Alignment.
Step 2) Connect With Your Body.
Step 3) Enjoy Your Food.
Step 4) Exercise Daily to Connect With and Tune Your Body.
Step 5) Clear the Channel.

I need to point out that these steps are not sequential, but concurrent. That means we don't do Step 1, "finish it" and then move on to Step 2. We do all five steps all the time. They are all inter-related, each affecting the other. Just like Life.

I also said these steps are simple. And they are. But simple does not necessarily mean they are easy – especially that first step that demands that you radically and completely change the way you think. It requires you to be able to tune out all of the marketing messages that are constantly bombarding you in this mass media culture.

So this will take work – and practice. But I promise you – It is worth it. You *can* do this. You *can* be free – be happy – and have a body that you love.

Part Three

The Science, Spirituality & Psychology of Weight Loss

There are more things in heaven and earth, Horatio,
than are dreamt of in your philosophy.

~ Shakespeare

Chapter 8

What About the Science?

We will discuss how to actually apply and live the steps and principles of Happy Calories Don't Count® a bit later. First, we need to address things like, "What about the science?"

My college calculus professor had a Far Side cartoon taped to his office door. It was a single panel illustration of a bookcase full of books, flames, and a devilish looking character. The titles of these books were things like *Story Problems*, *More Story Problems*, *The Big Book of Story Problems*, and *Story Problems Galore*. This was Hell's Library. The joke, of course, is that nobody likes story problems. They are the bane of every math student. Rather than simply solving equations (which may already be hard enough), we need to determine the relevant information and subsequent equations necessary to solve the problem given by a "story." In the beginning, the stories are relatively simple. They ask us things like how many candy bars can we buy if we have a dollar and each candy bar costs twenty-five cents. (Yes, these are last century prices.) But by the time we reach calculus, these problems become quite complex and devilish. Yes, we all hate story problems. But they do teach us a valuable lesson. They teach us a *process* for problem solving.

Story problems teach us how to solve even complex life problems. One of my most important realizations was that oftentimes that nasty textbook offered up additional information within the context of the story that was irrelevant to solving the problem at hand. I learned an important strategy: 1) What is it, exactly, that we are trying to solve – what is the answer we are looking for? 2) What information is needed to find this answer? 3) How do we put the information together to determine the answer?

This is important because in the context of finding freedom from food, body and weight issues, a lot of "science" is simply that extra irrelevant information.

Now I have a great respect for science. This discussion is in no way belittling science, the scientific community or the scientific contributions made to society. Rather, this is about viewpoints, perspectives and agendas – very few of which have anything to do with supporting you in your quest for healing and transformation.

To be able to learn to trust yourself you must realize that just because something is "science," that does not mean that it is "right." There were times when astronomers created complex equations to rationalize a universe in which the sun revolved around the earth. And now, of course, we know that the earth revolves around the sun. Until relatively recently, the atom was believed to be the smallest bit of matter. Now, quantum physics provides a whole new field of exploration. Science does the best it can with what information it has at the moment. And when new discoveries are made, the science evolves. Science does not know everything – and it does not necessarily know what is right for *you*.

Furthermore, scientific theories and studies are created by human minds operating from within their own individual frameworks and assumptions. As in the previous astronomy example, there was a time when the assumption was that the earth was the center of the universe. So the math equations were developed in a way that could explain and support that assumption. To even create other mathematical models, one had to be able to envision the idea of a different premise – mainly that the earth revolved around the sun (a premise that was downright dangerous during certain eras).

In terms of weight loss, a lot of scientific research is done from within the framework of the "diet and exercise" model. A lot of studies are conducted about food or exercise – as if food and exercise are the only components that make us human. Many studies have been conducted on the psychology of dieting – and how we succeed or fail (at treating our body like a caloric balance sheet) based on stress, support systems and other factors. No research (to my knowledge) has been done outside the "diet and exercise" paradigm and includes the *totality of who we are as human beings.* And this is, in part, because a "scientific" inquiry needs to address a reasonably small set of variables in order to reach any sort of conclusion.

Moreover, science only ever answers the question "what." It does not answer "why." Science can tell us that water freezes at 32 degrees Fahrenheit, but it cannot tell us *why.* Granted, a scientist might answer something like, "molecules get so cold that their movement slows down and they hook to each other to make a solid." But that still does not answer the question, *why.*

And this is important because in the weight loss arena, people make all sorts of assumptions and claims as to "why" someone gains or loses weight when they really have no basis to do so. Most scientific studies do *not* establish causality.

And this leads us to one of the biggest problems with "science" and weight loss. Have you ever tried to actually read a legitimate, scientific research study? There are so many qualifiers and statements about the design of the study that most lay people get frustrated, lost or bored. Ultimately most people just want the bottom line. This "essential gist" is at best, incomplete and at worst, misleading. (And, of course, this "gist" is what commands all of the media headlines and sound bites.) Furthermore, studies have outliers. So, if you are trying to apply the results of a scientific study to your own life, how do you know you are not the outlier?

Ultimately, the biggest problem with the "science of weight loss" is that it simply becomes nothing more than (perhaps irrelevant) information floating around in your head. It is information that you end up using to judge yourself. And it is information that creates interference in the messages you receive from your body.

As noted earlier, scientific studies cannot look at the entire body as a whole – there are too many variables. But your body is a whole. And your body is part of the bigger organism that is you. Your body works in harmony with your thoughts, your feelings, your beliefs, your dreams, your desires and your actions.

From a Happy Calories Don't Count® perspective, "the science of weight loss" ultimately does not tell us anything meaningful or actionable – especially when it comes to improving our relationships with our bodies and finding freedom from food drama. What is meaningful and actionable is tuning into the wisdom and guidance coming forth from our own unique bodies.

Chapter 9

The Milkshake Experiment

In the last chapter, I illustrated why science — in all of its glory — really does not have much to offer in terms of helping you heal and transform your pain around food, exercise, your body and your weight. The irony is that in this chapter I use a scientific study to support the Happy Calories Don't Count® principles, which *will* help you create a body and life you love.

I offer you "The Milkshake Experiment." Stanford professor Dr. Alia Crum[3] focuses on how subjective mindsets — the perspectives through which information

---

3   *https://mbl.stanford.edu/people*

is perceived, interpreted and organized – can influence objective reality through behavioral, psychological and physiological mechanisms. Basically, she is into the placebo effect. And since we all know about the placebo effect in medicine (a beneficial effect attributed to the patient's belief in the treatment because they really just took a sugar pill), Dr. Crum designed an experiment to see if there is a placebo effect with food. Spoiler Alert! There is.

In her experiment, Dr. Crum made a huge batch of milkshakes. She labeled some of the milkshakes as low calorie and some of the milkshakes as high calorie. The milkshakes were *exactly the same* – only the labels were different. So, some people *thought* they were drinking low calorie milkshakes and some people *thought* they were drinking high calorie milkshakes. After the participants enjoyed their milkshakes, blood was drawn, and tests were done. And wouldn't you know it, there were differences in the levels of this hormone called ghrelin between the two groups. Dr. Crum found that objective reality (ghrelin levels) was indeed influenced through a psychological mechanism (the milkshake label indicating calories, with all of our emotional baggage that goes along with it).

Now if you look up ghrelin, you will see that it is known as the "hunger hormone." So there are all sorts of people out there who like to use this experiment as proof that "your thoughts create your reality" and will tell you that if you want to lose weight, you just need to think and believe certain things about the food you eat. But that is crazy-making, magical wish fulfillment. (And it undermines your communication and relationship with your body!) We will discuss the spirituality and metaphysics of all of this in the next chapter. As far as the Milkshake Experiment goes, simply let it be sufficient "scientific proof" that a milkshake is not just a milkshake. A salad is not just a salad. Your thoughts, feelings and beliefs do matter.

Chapter 10

Physics and Metaphysics - The Law of Attraction

"Your Thoughts Create Your Reality." I do not think there is a single concept that is more misinterpreted, misunderstood or misused than the Law of Attraction. Since this topic can be as triggering as the word "fat," as scary as the fact that we cannot control our bodies, and as inconceivable as the idea that a lot of science is irrelevant to our task at hand (transforming diet drama into freedom, peace and happiness), let's walk it back a bit to see how we got here in the first place.

We come to spirituality, metaphysics and the Law of Attraction because things aren't going so great. In fact, they're awful. We feel bad about our bodies and ourselves because, despite our best efforts, we cannot seem to stick to a diet or exercise program – or the programs are not working. We have checked our hormones, been tested for allergies, and eliminated gluten, sugar and dairy. We may have even been to counseling or therapy. We have dealt with our inner child and our inner critic. And we finally forgave our mother for teaching us that food is love by giving us a cookie when we fell and skinned our knee when we were six. But we still can't figure out what's "wrong" (with us) – why it won't "work" – why we cannot lose the weight or get the body that we want. We are in pain and we want the pain to stop.

So, we look for answers. We might wander through the bookstore or see a flyer for some workshop that is going to teach us these "secrets of manifestation." We are going to learn how to use the power of our thoughts to get what we want (we're specifically discussing weight and body, but the "secrets" work for everything – romances, careers, money). We believe that when we finally "manifest" this thing we want, the pain will end and we will be free.

So we read these books and go to these workshops

that teach us all about our thoughts and vibrations and visualization. There is a part of us that does feel like maybe we are trying to make a magic trick happen with the Universe. But we ignore that little voice. We are in so much pain that we try our very best to believe this stuff is real. After all, String Theory in quantum physics says the entire universe is made up of vibrations. And we all know that visualization is part of an elite athlete's training program. We also feel good about the path we are taking because it is wrapped up in spirituality. Legitimate and well-respected authors write about this stuff. Buddha himself is quoted as saying, "All that we are is a result of what we have thought" and "What we think we become." And this is just another take on the corporate motivational slogan, "Your attitude determines your altitude."

"We are not silly or stupid," we say to that little voice. "We are open-minded and intelligent." Furthermore, these books and workshops point to others who have successfully manifested their dreams – we have proof that it works. So we are going to learn how to become enlightened and use our spiritual power to "create our day" and finally solve our mundane problems.

But our problems do not get solved. The pain

does not end. (In fact, sometimes the pain gets even worse!) The pain does not end because we have confused legitimate spiritual truth with wish fulfillment.

I know this is a lot, so let's make some sense out of this. A standard, basic Law of Attraction workshop or book will teach you something like this:

1. The entire universe is made up of energetic vibrations. (That's cool – string theory in quantum physics says that).

2. Vibrations with a similar frequency are attracted to each other. (The "Law" of Attraction).

3. Our current life circumstances are a product of things being "attracted" into our reality by the vibrations we are giving off.

4. To change our life circumstances, we can change our vibrations to match what we desire and then that Law of Attraction will bring us those new circumstances.

5. We can change our vibrations through various ways – by changing our thoughts (thoughts are energy), by meditation, by vi-

sualizing what we desire, by creating dream boards, by reciting affirmations, etc.

So far, so good. Nothing seems too far "out there." It seems to make sense. So let's use an example that has nothing at all to do with weight or body image, but is still pretty universal; let's use the example of money. We all need money to survive and we all have probably had times in our life when money was a little tighter than we would like.

If we look at the issue of money from the way I just described the Law of Attraction, it naturally follows that our abundance – or lack thereof – is a direct result of our energetic vibrations. Whatever our current financial state – it is so because of the energetic vibrations we are sending out into the universe (oftentimes through our thoughts). So we can change our financial state just by changing what we think (and vibrate). This is what a lot of people understand is happening when they hear the phrase, "Your thoughts create your reality."

I know. At first blush it is very empowering, and on the surface their logic seems to make sense. But let's go back and look at it again. The Law of Attraction –

taught or learned through a wish-fulfillment perspective – implies that if you think abundantly enough, if you could have the right vibrations, you could win the lottery. Now I don't presume to know everything in the Universe and I have no intention of being a killjoy. If winning the lottery is your dream, I hope you win. The reason winning the lottery is such a good example is *not* because the odds are so low. The lottery is a good example because it is *exclusively a game of chance.* There is no rhyme, reason, skill or effort involved. By definition, the outcome of a game of chance cannot be predicted, manipulated, or controlled. But the logical conclusion to the premise and reasoning of how the Law of Attraction is often taught is that we *could* win the lottery – we *could* control that outcome if we just got our vibrations right. And this is why the Law of Attraction teachers are always dealing with questions about winning the lottery and why they are always back-pedaling or talking around it saying things like, "We can 'win the lottery' in many ways." Whether it is intentional or not, they are teaching wish-fulfillment not Spiritual Truth.

Here is another way of looking at how many Law of Attraction teachers teach wish-fulfillment. (It's a preview of our Spiritual Truth discussion). Let's say your financial circumstances are represented by a three-dimensional cube.

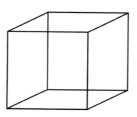

Let's say you do not like your current financial circumstances. A wish-fulfillment approach to the Law of Attraction implies that you can use your thoughts to change this cube into something else – a sphere or a pyramid perhaps. When viewing the Law of Attraction teachings from this angle, the unfeasibility of the wish-fulfillment method becomes clear.

Now let's take a look at all of this Law of Attraction stuff from a Spiritual Truth perspective.

1. The entire universe is made up of energetic vibrations. (That's cool – string theory in quantum physics says that).

2. Vibrations with a similar frequency are attracted to each other. (The "Law" of Attraction).

3. Our current life circumstances are a product of things being "attracted" into our reality by the vibrations we are giving off. (Perhaps. Perhaps not.)

4. To change our life circumstances, we can change our vibrations to match what we desire and then that Law of Attraction will bring us those new circumstances. (FALLACY! FALLACY! FALLACY!)

5. We can change our vibrations through various ways – by changing our thoughts (thoughts are energy), by meditation, by visualizing what we desire, by creating dream boards, by reciting affirmations, etc. (Yes! Absolutely – embrace your personal power!)

Did you notice the big FALLACY! FALLACY! FALLACY! in there? It is the exact same fallacy as the diet and exercise model! Yes, we are absolutely responsible for what we eat and what we do for exercise. But the fact that we are *responsible* for what we eat and what we do for exercise *does not mean that we can therefore control* our body and our weight through diet and exercise. Yes, we are absolutely *responsible* for our thoughts, feelings, beliefs, and vibrations. But the fact that we are responsible for our thoughts, feelings, beliefs and vibrations *does not mean that we can therefore control* what the Universe brings into our experience!

Once again, one of two things is probably happening about right now: relief or panic. The relief comes from realizing that you really do not control everything in the universe. Your relief comes from being let off the metaphorical metaphysical hook. You didn't not-get-that-thing you wanted simply because you could not really make yourself believe something that a part of you thought was ridiculous. You didn't do (or think) anything wrong! You are relieved to know that you really cannot compel your beliefs. You cannot make yourself think or believe something you really don't – just to try to get something you think you want. And you are relieved to have that truth confirmed (so you didn't "fail" at Law of Attraction). Moreover, from that wish-fulfillment perspective, the other logical conclusion is that any negative experience – anything bad that comes into your life – is your fault! You "attracted it" with your thoughts and vibrations. So the relief comes from finally being free from that mind loop of feeling bad about the bad thing you somehow "created" but knowing that feeling bad will only bring more bad but not knowing how to feel good when you really feel bad which is only going to bring more bad. (If you got crazy reading that sentence imagine what it feels like to live it.) The relief comes from understanding that your pain is not your fault and that sometimes, bad things happen to good people. The panic, however, comes from the fear of not being able to control the outcome. If you cannot control the outcome, how will you know you will be ok? You might still be in pain. Life might still be really, really awful. So how can you fix it?

Let's look at how to do this from a Spiritual Truth perspective. Take a look at the cube on the following page.

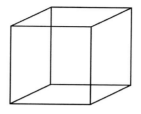

Is the cube coming down to the left? Or is it going up to the right? After a second or so you will be able to see it both ways. Now try to make it go down and left. Now try to make it go up and right. How are you doing that? By focusing your thoughts! This is an honest-to-goodness, real life example of "Your thoughts create your reality."

This cube is a metaphor for every single moment in your life. Every moment in your life can be seen in different ways. Now here is where things get interesting. If you look at that metaphorical life cube in one way (down and left), you will not be able to see what is on the back, bottom or left side of the cube. If you look at that metaphorical cube in another way (up and right), you will not be able to see what is on the top, back or right side. So just by the perspective you happen to choose, you see part and you miss part of "reality."

Let these different sides of the cube represent

the different actions you can take in the given moment of life. If you practice using the power of your thoughts to look at the cube in different ways, you will see more options available to you. This is important because the actions you take, based on the options you believe are available to you, based on the way you choose to view the situation (the metaphorical cube) could take you down a completely different path of life than other actions you could have taken from that same (metaphorical cube) moment based on options you did not know you had because of the way you chose to look at the situation. This is how you can navigate your life based on the idea that "your thoughts create your reality." Your thoughts won't change the cube into something else — a sphere or a pyramid. Your thoughts help you see all the options available to you so that you can make the most informed and empowered choices and actions. These choices and actions result in new life circumstances. *This* is how "your thoughts create your reality."

Metaphysics aside, your thoughts really do create your reality from a psychological perspective too. I don't remember much about high school. I spent most of my senior year in the hospital for anorexia. I do remember receiving loads of "Get Well" cards and letters from class-mates. And I remember being upset by them – they were "proof" of the fact that I was unlovable. To me, it looked like one of the other cheerleaders simply decided to get a card and have everyone sign it – because that would be the cool and popular thing to do. And, of course, people would sign it because they wanted to feel good about themselves too - like they were part of the gang offering support. The notes were so banal and generic – "We miss you! Come back soon!" No one really cared. No one *could* care. I was completely and utterly unlovable.

Well, I found that old box of cards and letters a while back and the experience of reading them was over-whelming. I am a lot older (and hopefully a little wis-er) and I was stunned by the love and support coming from the letters. Of course these notes sounded pedestri-an! They were written by seventeen-year-old kids! They were written by teenagers who did not have the emotion-al or communication skills to connect in any sort of deep, meaningful way. But that did not take away from their genuine care and affection for me. They were also writ-ten by kids who were watching their classmate disappear right in front of them at a time when hardly anyone even knew what anorexia was. They didn't know *what* to say. And then I saw it and the floor fell out from under me. "Take care and remember that I love you." *What?!?!?* This was written by a boy I'd had some classes with. We were friends, but not boyfriend and girlfriend. I had no idea he had even liked me. I saw another note from another boy. I did not date him either, but he wrote that he missed me too. I honest-to-God had never seen these notes before. They had been there all along, but I could not see them. I had believed I was so unlovable that I literally could not see what was written there in black and white.

It has taken thirty-some years and a lot of personal work to come to a place where I could see the love. It made me a bit sad. What could life have been like had I been able to see the love then? How could my life have been different? Our thoughts literally create our reality.

I know this is sounding complicated. Our thoughts create our reality – literally. But we can't just think something and have it magically manifest. So what do we actually *do??* **How** do we use our personal and spiritual power to create a body and life we love? It comes back to that Model of Alignment. Here's the picture again.

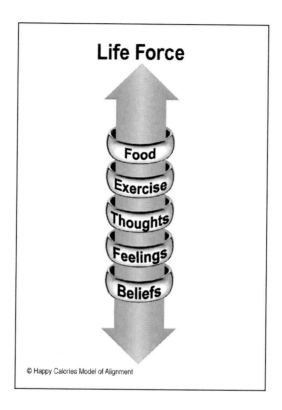

© Happy Calories Model of Alignment

From a wish fulfillment Law of Attraction perspective, they will tell you to "align your thoughts and vibrations with Source energy" to have Law of Attraction bring you what you want. (But we already know that is a crazy making fallacy that does not work.) Source Energy is defined as the ultimate – as God – as Life Force – or as whatever your belief system tells you is the highest and greatest. They tell you that you are supposed to align with the highest and greatest to get what you want. (If you were really that enlightened would you really even care about that thing anymore anyway??) So you do your best to align with Source Energy. You do your affirmations and your meditations, your dream boards and your scripting, you "create your day" and work hard at feeling good (which is supposed to bring you close to Source Energy – which will bring you what you want). You do all the stuff they teach you how to do. Then you wait. And you wait some more. Then you start to wonder. You check and look around to see if what you want is really coming, which suddenly becomes "lack thinking" which according to Law of Attraction will only bring you more lack. It is circular crazy making at its finest. So then you get worried and start to feel bad. And you try to feel better but you can't. You get stuck because your feelings are tied to an end result.

This is when I typically make that audacious suggestion that perhaps you might want to feel better simply because feeling better just feels better than feeling bad! Feeling better is its own reward. It just feels better! But let's not get sidetracked - back to the Model of Alignment.

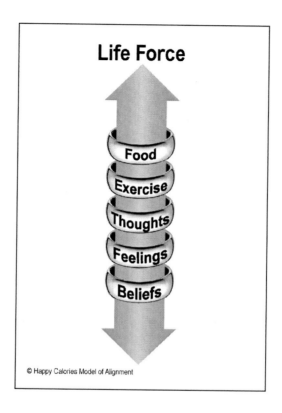

Rather than trying to align yourself with Source Energy, **Align with Yourself and allow Source Energy to flow through you.** Use all of those tools you have learned so well – the affirmations, the meditations, the visualizations, the pivoting, the positive psychology, etc. to help you harmonize your thoughts, feelings, beliefs and actions. That is the key. The tools are powerful, but the tools are not magic. Affirmations are not magic words that deliver magical results like "Open Sesame." Affirmations and all the other tools are powerful because they can help you change the way you think and feel. They can help you bring yourself into harmony with yourself. And when you are Aligned with yourself you are reconciled. You have no discord. So you feel at peace. You feel free. You are happy. You become an open channel for Life Force to flow powerfully and effectively through you. And from a mystical, metaphysical point of view, in this state you are literally vibrating *with* Source Energy because it is running through you. You can relax. You know that you are doing your part, so you can let go and let Life do its part.

Now here is an interesting paradoxical twist. Just because you are Aligned with yourself so that Life Force can flow powerfully through you, that does not necessarily mean you will get that external thing you want. Remember?? Fallacy!! You create your reality, but you cannot control your reality. You are responsible for your thoughts, feelings, beliefs, actions and getting congruent with yourself, but you are not in charge of the outcome. Life is in charge! But that also means that not getting that thing you want is through no fault of your own – so you can be at peace with it. You are freed from any stress or anxiety about it. And the best part is, when you are Aligned with yourself and Life Force is flowing through you – and you are literally vibrating with Source Energy – you are happy. And that is the only reason you wanted that external thing in the first place – you thought having it would make you happy. So you truly can have happiness without that thing. But I promise that this is not some sort of psychological "trick" – I do want you to get that thing you want. And a state of happiness (when you are congruent with yourself and Life Force is running through you) is the best shot you have of actually getting that thing to come into your experience. But in the meantime, either way, you are at peace. You got what you really wanted – happiness.

Chapter 11

Hungry for Happiness

"I have learned that it's all about being happy." That's how I began *Happy Calories Don't Count (neither does unhappy exercise)*. I have learned a lot more since writing that book, but I still maintain its core premise: we only want anything we want – including the body that we want – because we think having it will make us happy. Of course there are a lot of pop psychologists out there – and probably actual psychologists too – who will question that premise. "Will having that body (or man or job or house or whatever) *really* make you happy? What is it you *really* want?" And I still maintain that happiness is what we really want – we are literally "hungry" for happiness! I don't question the motivation for happiness – I believe you when you say you want that body (or man or job or house or whatever) because you think it will make you happy. I question the approach. If we are engaged in some sort of diet or exercise program to get the body that we want (because we think getting that body would make us happy), but the experience of the diet or exercise program is in any way making us unhappy, we experience a dissonance. We will not be able to achieve that which we ultimately desire – happiness.

Which brings us to the topic of "emotional eating." I know that may have seemed like a non sequitur, but it really is not. A lot of people use "hungry for happiness" as a metaphor for emotional eating (you aren't really "hungry," what is it you *really* want? Happiness??). There are entire sections in bookstores dedicated to books that explore all of the "emotional" reasons that we eat. The psychology and spirituality of food issues is a really hot topic - and with all due respect, I call BS on all of that. Yes – I just said a very unladylike thing. The truth is not always pretty, but it will set you free.

Now I am in no way minimizing anyone's pain

surrounding the issue. Believe me – I have been there and done that. I have the t-shirt and wrote the book![4] And I fully understand and respect how food is used symbolically in various cultures and spiritual practices. But when it comes to the traditional notion of "emotional eating" (eating for reasons other than physical hunger, often to soothe some emotional upset) and how to heal all of the pain and dysfunction this "emotional eating" creates, I call BS. Again, unladylike... this just illustrates what a big deal this point is!!

You see, "emotional eating" is really only a problem in the context of the "diet and exercise" model. And everyone is going around trying to heal emotional eating from *within* the context of that model! In the "diet and exercise" model, our bodies are essentially a caloric balance sheet and we only get so many calories to eat. Therefore, to eat for "emotional" reasons – to eat for reasons other than physical hunger – is not a good use of that daily allotment of calories. So, we jump through all sorts of hoops to try to make sure that we only eat for physical hunger (otherwise we will have to pay the price of exercise or weight gain). We play mind games

---

4   *Happy Calories Don't Count (neither does unhappy exercise)*

to question our "real" motivations for eating. We make up little reward systems and find other (expensive) ways to nurture ourselves instead of food. Facials, mani/pedis and new shoes, for example. We go to therapy or read self-help books to heal our inner child and intimacy issues. We work on our low self-esteem and inner critic that always seem to sabotage our success. We even get treatment for diagnosed eating disorders. We do all this work, but we still have to deal with the food! We do all this emotional and spiritual work from *within a framework* that says we only get so much to eat. So, no matter how healed, enlightened or evolved we become, there is still that itchy splinter in our hearts and minds.

Just for fun, let's take all of the emotion out of it and look at this logically. Why do we eat for physical hunger in the first place? We eat for physical hunger because *being hungry doesn't feel good!* Thus, eating for physical hunger is also "emotional" – it is an attempt to feel better. All eating is "emotional." "Emotional" eating is not a problem. But the Alice in Wonderland Rabbit Hole we can fall into trying to heal our emotional eating really is a big problem. We end up questioning and second-guessing every bite and every "motivation." This not only makes us crazy, it does something much worse. It disconnects us from our body and teaches us that we cannot trust it.

Eating to feel better will always work. *It is the eating to not feel bad that never works and gets us into trouble.* It is a subtle, but very significant distinction: eating to feel better vs. eating to not feel bad. And the difference is not between "good" and "bad." *It is between feeling and not feeling.* We can never *not* feel. That is why "emotional eating" is so awful. We feel bad, then we eat to not feel bad, but then we feel bad for eating (likely because we believe we have just screwed up that caloric balance sheet), and we try to not feel bad, so we eat some more, which just makes us feel bad again. It is a crazy vicious circle. Eating to not feel bad will never work. But eating to feel better will always work – for as soon as you stop feeling better, you naturally stop eating. You don't stop because some external voice is telling you "that is all you are allowed to eat." You don't stop because you are not sure about your emotional or spiritual "motivation." You stop because to continue to eat simply would not feel better. All of the stress and mind games are gone. And how do you really *know* you would not continue to feel better if you kept eating?

You know because you are connected with your body!!

That is the beauty of the 5 Step Method of Happy Calories Don't Count®! We no longer think in terms of that calories in/exercise out balance sheet. "Diet and Exercise" is gone! So we don't have to worry about why we eat, what we eat or how much. We are guided to our food choices by our zest for life and our connection with our body. We can enjoy our food without any stress or drama. And as soon as eating whatever stops helping us feel better, we stop eating. In this context, I would argue that "emotional eating" is actually a *good* thing! Our feelings are our guide.

Feelings are our guide, huh? For some, this may sound a lot like Law of Attraction speak again. For others, this may sound a lot like "Intuitive Eating" – which is often used interchangeably with "Conscious Eating" or "Mindful Eating." For the uninitiated, this book may seem like a big lesson on Intuitive, Conscious or Mindful eating. But to me, this is really more than a simple semantic issue. How do you arrive at a state in which you can eat intuitively or mindfully? It cannot happen as long as the "diet and exercise" model is around. I have seen Intuitive, Conscious and Mindful Eating coaches put their clients on diets to "learn how to listen to their bodies." Excuse me? How can you learn to listen to your body when you are on a diet? Food aside, these approaches can become almost as head-spinning-crazy-making as the wish-fulfillment perspective of the Law of Attraction or the Alice in Wonderland Rabbit Hole of "emotional eating." How do you know it is really your intuition and not your own "self-sabotaging behavior?" And this idea of being "conscious" or "mindful" can quickly turn into judgmental head games.

So rather than intuitive or mindful, I like to say that Happy Calories Don't Count® is "bodyful." It is a body-centered approach. We let our body lead the way. And we can do that because we have ditched the "diet and exercise" model and Embraced a Model of Alignment (Step 1). And because we have done that, we have the space and grace to Connect with Our Body (Step 2). Then we really can trust our body and Enjoy our Food (Step 3). We Exercise Daily to Connect With and Tune Our Body (Step 4) to deepen that relationship, fine-tune our connection with our body, and further develop our communication and listening skills — so we can trust our impulses to eat and to stop eating.

And we use our personal growth and spiritual development tools to continually Clear the Channel (Step 5) so we can finally relax, trust ourselves and eat "intuitively."

Part Four

Food for Thought

Navigating the Reality of Living in this World

Those who see themselves as whole make no demands.

~ A Course in Miracles

Chapter 12

Media and Marketing Literacy

Now that you understand the Model of Alignment with the 5 Steps of the Happy Calories Don't Count® Method, and we have sorted out the emotional, psychological and spiritual issues of personal transformation, it is time to discuss some of the external factors with which we must contend – the reality of living in this world. This is all interrelated, so we will just walk through these ideas one step at a time.

We live in a mass media marketing driven society where we are constantly bombarded with images and sound bites that try to influence our state of being (usually to get us to buy something). That is a fact. But fighting against this does not create empowerment. Empowerment comes from developing media and marketing literacy skills – and using those skills to make conscious choices about the thoughts, feelings and beliefs we want to hold and the actions we want to take. Let's take a classic example – the digital retouching of media images (aka Photoshop) – and explore how uneducated perspectives can create – and perpetuate – more drama and dysfunction around our weight and our bodies.

A while back I stumbled upon a blog post written by an editor of a popular women's fitness magazine. The editor proudly argued why this particular magazine does not digitally retouch their cover models. She wrote:

> "A star's body is on the cover for a reason: to inspire all of us struggling with our weight (me included) that we, too – through hard work – can get a body like hers."

Did you catch that? That part about getting a "body like hers?" I hate to break it to that editor, but she will never have "a body like hers" – regardless of whether or not she follows the star's diet and exercise tips featured in the magazine article. (Which is why that model is on the cover in the first place – to sell the magazine, which promises to reveal her "secrets" for looking good.) The only person who will ever have a body like the cover model (Photoshopped or not) is that cover model. The editor will always have a body like her own. I will always have a body like mine. You will always have a body like yours. But that certainly does not mean that our bodies cannot be beautiful. And that does not mean that – through conscious effort – our bodies cannot be fit and strong and look their very best. And that does not mean that – through conscious effort – we cannot create bodies that we love. We can do all of those things! The only thing we cannot do is "get a body like hers."

The issue is not with the cover model – digitally retouched or not. The issue is this: with the skills of world-class magicians, master marketers misdirect our focus by teaching us to look outside of ourselves. The issue is that – through clever marketing – we are taught to believe that with hard work, we can get something we can never get – "a body like hers." Marketers teach us to believe that we can get a body – different from our own – if we only knew that cover model's diet and exercise secrets. They teach us these false beliefs and then use them to sell magazine articles featuring said model's diet and exercise tips.

This is not about bashing magazines, marketing or marketers. Marketers are not evil people. (In fact, some of them are quite clever and entertaining!) This is not about bashing Photoshop. Photoshop is not the problem. And as a side note, it is industry standard that every image published in mainstream media is given a once over. Granted, the client or art director may ask that the original shape, curves and laugh lines of the model remain, but there is always work done to spiff up the light and brightness of the image or adjustments in the color saturation at the very least. So for any magazine editor to flatly say images have not been retouched is stretching the truth a bit. But again, this is not about bashing or blaming anyone or anything. This is about developing your personal empowerment – through media and marketing literacy.

Let's step back and look at all of this from another angle. Why does everyone get so upset about Photoshop? Because it is "cheating?" Because it makes someone look different (thinner, younger, "better") than they really are? Because it creates a false sense of reality?

Well, that would all be based on an underlying assumption that photographs reflect reality in the first place.

Photographs do *not* reflect reality. You know that for yourself simply by the number of selfies you take before you pick one to upload to Facebook or Instagram! You flip that cell phone camera so you can see what you are looking at. You compose the shot so you can control the framing to look your best. You look for the best angle and the best lighting. And you take a bunch so you can pick the most flattering. You might even use one of those fancy filters that create really cool effects. You might even use one of those fancy new photo-editing apps to "touch up" things you don't like about yourself and help you "look better."

A photograph simply captures a certain lighting scheme in a window of space around a given subject in one very specific – never to be recreated – moment of time. Photographs are not reality. Photographs are a form of art.

When viewed from this perspective, it really does not matter if images are digitally retouched or not. Magazine covers and ads are works of art. Just think about the creative team that goes into producing that image! The art director, the set designer, the lighting designer, the makeup artist, the hair stylist, the wardrobe stylist, the Photoshop artist. Magazine covers and ads are artistic creations crafted by teams of highly skilled experts. Granted, these images have a purpose – to sell us something. But that does not take away from the fact that the image itself is a work of art.

The problem really never was with Photoshop – or the model. (In fact, the model is simply another prop in this work of art.) The problem is that we compare ourselves against that image. That is where all of the pain and anxiety and assaults on our self-esteem come from. The pain and anxiety come from us - from our own actions – from comparing ourselves to the external. But when we use our personal power to change the way we look at things, healing can occur. When we recognize that photographs are simply works of art, we can start to appreciate their beauty. (Spiritual Truth Speaking: Appreciating the beauty in others helps you see your own.) When we recognize that photographs are simply works of art, we stop comparing ourselves against them. We understand that to compare ourselves against a magazine cover would be just as silly as if we compared ourselves against the Mona Lisa!

And you know what? When you stop comparing yourself against magazine covers and ads you develop the mental, emotional and spiritual musculature to stop comparing yourself period. You stop comparing yourself to other women and you stop comparing yourself to the you of ten years ago. And when you let all of this comparing go, you create the space and grace to see and appreciate your own brilliance and your own beauty.

Speaking of your own brilliance and your own beauty, let's discuss those Body Image and Body Positivity movements. What comes to mind when you hear "body image" or "body positivity?" In my experience, most people think these phrases are basically interchangeable and refer to "loving your body" or "feeling good about your body." I see this as a problem.

Yes, I completely understand the irony of this given that one of the main objectives of this book is to teach you how to feel good in and about your body. And this is an important point. A primary objective of this book is to *teach*. Loving your body and feeling good about your body are very good things to do – but they are not things that can be compelled. Just like a belief, *love cannot be compelled.* You cannot compel yourself to love anything, let alone your body. You cannot compel your feelings either. (Yes – I know, I have just said some version of "compel" four times – that is because this is important!)

So within the context of the popular Body Image and Body Positivity movements a lot of women are left hanging. One of the Catch 22's of "body positivity" is the fact that most women *do not* feel good in or about their bodies. And without a process to take one from a place of body shame and pain to an authentic place of peace and freedom, a movement is simply a lot of hype. "Love the skin you're in!" is a great slogan for a body lotion, but it cannot help you love your body. Personal transformation is not a sound bite. It is very deep – and it is very personal.

Furthermore, these Body Positivity and Body Image movements/communities have the potential to create even more pain and shame because there is no room within the context of "body positivity" to feel any negativity toward your body. You already feel bad about your body – which is why you are trying this body positivity thing in the first place – but then all they do is tell you to love your body – which you cannot seem to figure out how to do because you really hate your body – so then you end up feeling bad because you cannot make yourself feel something you don't feel – and then you feel like a fraud around the others – so then you can't even do body positivity "right" which makes you feel worse.

But perhaps most importantly, the body positivity and body image movements fall miserably short because they fail to change the premise that is causing all of this body drama in the first place. (Thus, failing to create any real, meaningful change and perpetuating the unspoken pain and shame that plague so many.)

At their best the body positivity and body image movements say, "Don't diet and exercise to conform yourself to unrealistic societal standards of beauty! You are beautiful just the way you are!" And it is true that you are beautiful just the way you are! And it is good that they tell you that. But they also silently perpetuate the idea that you *could* conform to an unrealistic societal standard of beauty if you wanted to – if you just dieted and exercised. The body positivity and body image movements quietly, unwittingly perpetuate the pain because they never challenge or reject the fundamental premise of the "diet and exercise model" – let alone, reveal its flaw. They fail to understand what we have been discussing all along.

Yes, you are *responsible* for what you eat and what you do for exercise. But again, the fact that you are responsible for what you eat and what you do for exercise *does not mean you can therefore control* your body or your weight through diet and exercise. ***That*** is the fallacy – the hook in your heart that keeps you in pain. Once you realize it for what it is, a tremendous weight (pun intended) is lifted off your shoulders.

You recognize that your weight is neither your fault – nor to your credit. You are not to blame. You are freed from shame. And when you understand that you cannot control your body, you can start to partner with it. And partnering with your body is the quickest way to create authentic body positivity.

Chapter 13

Cultivating Your Greatest Relationship

So how exactly do you "partner" with your body? You simply build a relationship with your body just like you would with any other person. The process itself is really simple. And you have had plenty of practice – you have been doing it your whole life. It is just that you have had all of these other things going on that seem to complicate the issue.

Acceptance, for example. Acceptance is a concept that is tossed around a lot in psychology and spirituality. But so many of us struggle so much with accepting ourselves and our bodies. Why? We struggle because there is absolutely no room for acceptance within the "diet and exercise" model. At best, acceptance would be coming to terms with the "reality of your situation" so that you would then take action to change it.

But more often, acceptance would mean giving up – it would mean defeat. The assumption is that if we accepted our body the way it is right now, we would not have the internal motivation necessary to do the work of a diet or exercise program to change it. So acceptance is not tolerated. And that "diet and exercise" model is woven right into the very fabric of our culture – which means that the resistance to self-acceptance continually seeps into our consciousness.

We can also resist accepting something because of fear. We fear (based on the diet and exercise model) that if we accept our body the way it is right now, it won't change. We fear that if we accept our life circumstances the way they are right now, they won't change.

But acceptance does not mean giving up wanting what you want. Acceptance is to *give up the pain* around not having what you want in this particular moment. When you accept – when you release the pain – you have more peace and freedom and bandwidth to actually do anything that might be necessary for you to do to create the changes in your life that you would like to see.

This idea of releasing the pain is important. As we have already discussed, feelings cannot be compelled. That is why I am often at odds with Louise Hay. Now don't get me wrong. I love Louise Hay. During a dark time in my life, I wrote her a letter – and she wrote me back! Louise was the real deal. She walked her talk, and she is the gold standard against whom everyone else is measured. But just because she happened to find success with her affirmations and mirror work, that does not mean it works for everyone. So I am here to help fill that gap.

Just in case you have no idea who or what I am talking about, let me explain. Louise Hay is considered the grandmother (or godmother) of personal growth and self-help, especially from a metaphysical perspective. And she was big on self-love. So she taught us how to repeat affirmations of self-love. *"I love myself just the way I am."* And she taught us to do this while looking into a mirror. This action is theoretically supposed to help us reprogram our brains so that we will indeed eventually love ourselves.

Well guess what. If you really hate yourself, standing in front of a mirror repeating over and over to yourself that you love yourself is likely to bring up a lot of resistance and pain. You know you are just trying to convince yourself of something that is not true. And that resistance is very smart and logical! *You do not want to trick yourself!* You want to be honest, authentic and congruent with yourself. So if standing in front of a mirror repeating over and over to yourself that you love yourself does not make you feel better – if it just creates frustration and pain – stop doing it!

I want you to **stop** doing the things that cause you pain! Stop repeating words that are not true. Stop looking at yourself in the mirror. Stop doing all of those millions of tiny little things you do all day long (perhaps even unconsciously) that undermine your sense of self and self-esteem. Stop checking to see if you have cellulite on your butt. Stop pinching the rolls around your middle. Stop looking for new lines on your face. Stop hating yourself.

You do not need to do any work at all to love yourself - simply stop hating yourself. Then you will feel better. Then you will have some internal space. You will feel a little freer. And you will eventually be able to allow self-love to bloom naturally.

Now I just went on a little rant about all of the things

you should stop doing – all the little things that keep you in a state of pain and despair. Well oftentimes, it is not *what* you are doing, but *how*. It is the state of consciousness you are in when you do that thing. Take looking in a mirror, for example. Snow White's wicked stepmother was right. Mirrors are magical. Mirrors are magical because they do not reflect physical reality – they reflect our state of being – and they will always give us what we seek.

The issue is not really the mirror itself. The issue is our intention – our motivation. Are we simply looking for information and evaluating potential actions based on what we see? Are we checking to see if we have spinach in our teeth or if our hair is a bit disheveled? Or are we looking for judgment – searching for those emerging wrinkles – signs that we are somehow failing at defying age? There is a shocking – but all too realistic – scene in the movie *Mean Girls* in which the newest member of the clique watches in confusion as the other popular girls engage in a bonding ritual of picking themselves apart in front of a mirror. That magic mirror will always give us what we seek. If we are looking for beauty, we will find it. But if we are looking for condemnation, we will most certainly find that.

Speaking of beauty – which is in the eye of the beholder – you know how there is always that one woman whose beauty and body just seem to make you feel "less than?" Well first off, *she* is not making you feel "less than" – you are doing that. You are doing that by comparing yourself against her. There is a small part of you that thinks she must "really have it together" to look so good. You think that because there is still a part of you operating from that underlying core default "diet and exercise" model. That model says, "She looks good so she must be working out and watching her food." And because she is successful at that, she must be motivated, disciplined and smart. But you don't think that you look as good as she does (whether you are following your own diet and exercise program or not). You think that somehow you are not as motivated or disciplined or smart. You think that you cannot seem to get your life together to get yourself to look the way she looks. So, you feel "less than."

Well, let me fill you in on some little secrets. These come from over twenty years in a Pilates Studio and ten years of Happy Calories®. Of course, we all know that "everybody is different" (that is the standard diet disclaimer after all). But do you really know how different every *body* actually is?

For better or for worse, your body shape and size is only partly based on things you can control – like being in Alignment with your food choices and your daily Happy Exercise® (during which you connect with and tune your body), and all of the other steps we have covered. For better or for worse, your body shape and size is *mostly* based on things over which you have no control – like the proportions of your skeleton, the structure of your joints, and the flexibility of your less stretchy connective tissues. (And for the record, *no one* has a perfect body.) But you see this woman and you attribute her good looks to some sort of inherent virtue she must have – which you "obviously do not have." So you end up feeling bad. But this story could not be further from the truth! This woman may indeed make efforts to optimize her appearance and I am not discounting any work or effort she does make. But she is working with a physical structure and components that she inherited from genetics or God (whatever you prefer to believe). She can claim no personal credit or responsibility for it. So there is absolutely no reason for you to feel "less than."

We are each completely and utterly unique – at

the most fundamental levels – there *is* *no* comparison! Furthermore, in the deepest levels of her soul she knows that she cannot take personal credit for her good looks. On some level she knows she does not really have control – no matter what she eats (or doesn't) or what she does for exercise (or doesn't) – she knows she cannot control her body. She knows no matter what face cream she uses or procedure she has done she cannot control her aging beauty. And that scares her. So she is just as anxious and stressed out as you are.

Now can we all just let this comparison game go already? I know it is hard to do. In fact, it is the second-hardest thing I am asking you to do (giving up the "diet and exercise" model is number one). This comparison thing is an insidious – and oftentimes unconscious – habit. And if it goes unchecked, it never ends!! I watch women at country clubs and philanthropic organizations who are in their *seventies* and *eighties* size each other up in the comparison game. If you play this game the sad, painful joke ends up being on you. For when you are judging and sizing others up in comparison, you end up stressed out and anxious because you are actually judging yourself. The other interesting thing is that you are really projecting. You see someone you think is beautiful and project a shiny, happy, fabulous life onto her because you think you would be happy if you looked that way. So in your efforts to be like her (so you can be happy), you compare ourselves against her – which ultimately makes everyone unhappy. So stop comparing. I know it's hard. But I promise you it is worth it.

When we can let all of that comparison stuff go, it really is quite simple to build a relationship with our body. Think about pregnant women who get those crazy cravings for pickles and ice cream. Motherhood is a really strong instinct. Because of this, women will oftentimes allow themselves to connect with their body during the experience of pregnancy. They are a little more accepting of their body – for it is this amazing and powerful thing creating Life! They feel how their body changes with the new little miracle growing inside them. And they are more likely to allow themselves to eat those strange things they crave – because "it's for the baby." (Unfortunately, oftentimes once the baby is born, it's back to that diet and exercise program to lose the baby weight.) But we obviously do not need to become pregnant to "have an excuse" to ignore the "diet and exercise" model and connect with our body. We can simply choose to let all of that crazy-cultural-head-stuff go. When we do that, building a relationship with our body really is a natural thing to do. We use the same skills and tools that we use for any of our other great relationships.

I will show you. *(You may want to pause here and get out a pen and paper to take some notes – Hint Hint.)*

Think about your best friend. It does not matter who this person is. It could be a family member, friend, pet – living or deceased – it does not matter. Just bring to mind your very best friend.

What are the qualities that describe this relationship? (Write them down.)

How do you feel about yourself when you think about this relationship? (Write that down too.)

How do you feel about the other person? (You got it, write that down.)

How do *they* feel about *you*? (We're on a roll... you're

getting it!)

What do you give them?

What do *they* give *you*?

What do you receive? (Just because someone gives you something that does not mean you allow yourself to receive it.)

What is your role in this relationship?

What is it that you *know* about this other person?

What is it that they know about you?

What do they ask for in this relationship?

What do *you* ask of *them*?

What can you count on?

What can *they* count on?

Think about all the love and support and camaraderie and fun and depth and strength of this relationship. Now, what if *that relationship* were with your body... Think about how life-changing that would be! So start there. Start with treating your body like your best friend. And let your body be your best friend. Respect your body and communicate with it. Use that daily Happy Exercise® as "date time" to get to know your body and to learn how to hear what it is trying to tell you. Trust your body and teach it that it can trust you. It really is not that hard. It just takes getting all of that "diet and exercise" junk out of your head and a little practice. I promise you it is worth it. After all, you are going to be with your body for the rest of your life; so it can only serve you to develop a relationship with it.

Chapter 14

Subtle But Significant Distinctions

Ok, so now:

1. You know all the steps necessary to create a body and life you love.

> Step 1) Embrace a Model of Alignment
>
> Step 2) Connect with Your Body
>
> Step 3) Enjoy Your Food
>
> Step 4) Exercise Daily to Connect with and Tune Your Body
>
> Step 5) Clear the Channel

2. We have discussed this model in terms of science, metaphysics and spirituality, as well as the pop-psycholo-

gy of emotional eating.

3. I have given you perspectives and insights to help you navigate the reality of living in our mass media marketing, competitive culture.

4. I have helped you see that you really can develop a relationship with your body.

This chapter is all about the other very important things that did not make their ways into previous conversations. Everything is interrelated. But we cannot talk about everything at once because that would be too confusing and overwhelming (like Life can be). So these issues are the tangents I refrained from wandering down in previous chapters. Let's go.

I will start with a pop quiz. Did you notice that in the last chapter I said Louise Hay "is the gold standard against whom everyone else is measured" – but then turned around and offered up two pages telling you to stop the comparison game? To the uninitiated observer it may seem like I am contradicting myself. But I am not. Just like there is a very subtle – but significant – distinction between eating to feel better and eating to not feel bad, there is a very subtle – but very significant – distinction between *discernment and judgment.*

Discernment is simply using all of your powers of observation to gather information to make the best, most congruent decision, choice, or action you can make in the given moment. Judgment creates pain. Judgment comes back to bite you. (Pun intended.) Spiritual Truth Speaking: You cannot judge others without also judging yourself. And when you are playing that comparison game, I am guessing that more often than not it is a game of judgment rather than discernment.

When you judge others, you end up anxious and stressed out. And you cannot judge food – as good or bad – without also judging yourself. If you eat "good" food, then you are good. If you eat something "bad," then you are bad too. If you approach that magic mirror in the context of discernment, you can easily choose a figure flattering outfit and makeup look. If you approach it with judgment, everything you put on will "make you look fat" and you will see every flaw in your complexion.

This discernment vs. judgment thing is a very big deal. Not just in your own life, but in the lives of your children. Your children are watching you. And by that I don't mean that your children are watching what you eat and what you do for exercise — although they are doing that. They are also watching how you *relate* to what you eat and what you do for exercise and how you *relate* to yourself in the mirror. So the best way to help your children develop a strong sense of self and positive body image and self-esteem is to model it for them through your own transformation and healing.

Another thing I need to point out is that this "transformation and healing" does not mean that you suddenly do not care about your looks. It is ok to want to look pretty! It is ok to want to be fit! It is ok to want to feel like you look your very best! This can sound down-right blasphemous in the context of some of the body image/positivity and women's empowerment move-ments. I have seen a lot of pain and confusion get cre-ated because of "skinny shaming" or "pretty shaming." It seems like movements have become political and that the "embrace your curves" or "be yourself" mottos sug-gest that any desire to optimize or improve your health or appearance is a lack of self-acceptance and self-love. And this could not be further from the truth! You are allowed to want to look however you want to look. Make-up — no makeup. High fashion — capri length workout pants with long white tube socks. Size whatever. It is your right. The purpose of this book is not to influence what you think you want – but to help you create success on your own terms and to optimize your results.

And remember, the key to all of this (if someone held a gun to my head and said I could only tell you one thing) is to cultivate that relationship with your body. Your body is your partner in this grand adventure called Life. It has been with you since the day you were born, and it will be with you until the end. Your body needs you as much as you need it. Your body loves you. Your body wants you to be happy. Your body knows what it wants and needs to help make you happy. Your body is your GPS. Not just with food and exercise – but with Life itself. You know how there is this thing called "gut instinct." That is your body talking. Your Spidey Sense – that is your body too. So work on that relationship with your body.

Great relationships start with acceptance and respect. And they are built through listening and communicating. And they are not abusive. This is tricky. If you are someone who has had the horrific experience of being physically, sexually, or emotionally abused –

especially as a child – it could be quite easy to assume that your body was responsible for the assault. So, of course, you would have resistance to cultivating this relationship. If this is the case, please get professional help and support. Your body is not your enemy. In fact, it is your greatest ally. And you do not need to have suffered physical abuse at the hands of another. It is quite possible that your body has suffered abuse from you. The dieting, the starving, the bingeing, the body bashing workouts, the lack of movement, the shaming and the blaming – you do that! And after all of it, your body is still here for you. Think about that. Take a moment and thank your body. Becoming embodied truly is the key to healing everything. You cannot starve, over-eat, sit around and not move, or over train when you are embodied – it doesn't feel good! Feelings are your guide - happiness is your internal compass! When you are embodied, you can act from inspiration not desperation. When you are embodied, you instinctively create an optimized state of health, vitality, wellbeing and joy.

Now there are people out there who like to tell you to "fake it until you make it." I disagree with this. You don't want to fake it with your body or yourself. You want to be authentic, congruent and aligned. And I know all of this "connect with your body," "talk to your body" stuff may seem like something you don't know how to do (so you would have to fake it) – but I promise you, you do know how to do it.

Let me give you an example from a completely different subject. Acting. Actors need to learn how to become other people. They learn (or develop) their characters' wants, needs, motivations and relationships to the other characters in the story. You could look at it like actors are the epitome of "faking it." Many years ago I was in a play during which my character was on the phone with her mother. So, like a well-trained actress, I imagined and acted "my character's" motivation and relationship to "my character's" mother. Well one night my actual mother was in the audience. In fact, she was sitting right in front of me – in my line of sight. And I don't know where this crazy idea came from, but I somehow thought why not just talk to my mother? She is sitting right there. And so I did. That performance was a "breakthrough," giving me some of the best reviews of my theatrical career.

Don't fake it. Just talk to your body. It might feel strange or silly but just do it. Then breathe and drop into your body. Your body will answer you.

You really do have more power than you realize. You have all sorts of power - spiritual power, emotional power, intellectual power and economic power. With your spiritual and intellectual power you can choose perspectives that will support and enhance your sense of self while navigating our ever-changing world. With your economic power, you can be part of the change. I stand by and watch with frustration as many of the body image and women's "empowerment" movements fight against what currently is. They make all sorts of noise about unrealistic standards of beauty, models that are of only one body type, a lack of ethnic diversity, and Photoshop. Their form of "empowerment" is to make noise and to bully other women to agree with them and to "force" social and economic change. To me, that is not empowerment.

Empowerment comes from understanding how we all relate to one another. For example, companies *need* us to purchase their products and services. Without us, they cease to exist. So if we do not like the super-skinny-14-year-old-Photoshopped-single-ethnicity models offered up by a magazine or company, we can simply choose not to purchase their products or services. We have the power of the purse. And when we do not purchase products or services offered by a company, they will need to change their marketing strategy to court us.

Empowerment does not come from changing what is. (Trying to change the cube into a sphere.) Empowerment comes from changing how we relate to what is. (Looking at all of the different sides of the cube.) And paradoxically, when we change how we relate to what is, what is often changes. (Based on our choices and actions determined by our relationship to it.) It all comes back to relationships – and ultimately a personal choice. How you choose to view (and relate to) things directly impacts your experience of them – and your quality of life.

What I love about the Model of Alignment and the 5 Steps of Happy Calories Don't Count® is that they offer a framework where everything is addressed and everything "fits" – the physical, the metaphysical, the emotional, the spiritual, the psychological, the intellectual. All of those things we do, all of those things we study, all of those things we try - just to figure out how to scratch that itch, end the pain and get those physical results – all of it comes together. There is a place for everything – that puzzle is finally completed. And it comes to us in a nice neat little package with a bow on top. Even for those of us who are control-freaks-who-fear-that-life-won't-be-ok-if-we-don't-know-that-we-can-control-the-out-come-to-make-sure-it-will-be-ok can find some peace.

When we are congruent with ourselves, when we are in harmony with ourselves, when we are Aligned and the energy of Life Force can move through us, we become intimately connected with the divinity within. We *are* Life. We *are* Light. How can we not be beautiful? How can we not have worth? How can we not be loveable? How can we not be enough? *We can't!* We *can't* not be beautiful! We *can't* not have worth! We *can't* not be loveable! We *can't* not be enough! How can it not be ok? It's impossible! It *can't* not be ok. So just relax, take a deep breath and shine.

Part Five

An Appetite for Life

To live is the rarest thing in the world.
Most people just exist.

~ Oscar Wilde

Chapter 15

Hungry for Meaning

Compliments are interesting things. There are the generic "you look nice today" or "great job!" Compliments that feel good in the moment but are quickly forgotten. And yet these same positive affirmations can also elicit a negative response when the compliment is incongruent with the recipient's state of being. There are the compliments that are really insults in disguise. And there are also those compliments that stay with us – compliments that direct our lives through our desire to live up to them. The two most generous and meaningful compliments I've ever received are:

1) If reincarnation exists, I want to come back as your cat and 2) Your book *(Happy Calories Don't Count)* reminds me of Viktor Frankl's *Man's Search for Meaning.*

I read *Man's Search for Meaning* as a freshman in college. I remembered that it was a story of how Frankl had survived the Nazi concentration camps. But that was about it. I remembered that Frankl was an example of someone who could endure, survive and thrive. But I didn't remember the lessons his book taught.

Perhaps Frankl's work affected me more deeply than I knew. Or perhaps our work is shaped by similar struggles for survival. I find it interesting that one of the comments frequently made about people suffering from anorexia is that they "look like they have been in a concentration camp." Physically, it is obvious in severe cases when the skin just hangs on the bones. But what is not so obvious to the outsider is the mental, emotional, and spiritual toll eating disorders take. To be able to override every natural instinct your body has for survival, to be able to consciously and deliberately withhold food from yourself requires an "SS guard" in your mind inflicting mental torment. Frankl himself wrote that we all carry within us an "inner concentration camp," and upon a recent reading of *Man's Search for Meaning* there were many passages about which a voice in my head said, "check." Either way, I now know what that person meant by that compliment.

Viktor Frankl had something to say. And his message was grounded in the reality of Auschwitz, Dachau, and Türkheim rather than in some abstract psychological theories. I too have something to say. And my message is grounded in the reality — and self-healing — of an eating disorder (rather than in the accepted psychological theories about food and body issues). Interestingly, we both say essentially the same things!

In *Happy Calories Don't Count* I asserted that our primary, intrinsic motivation as human beings is happiness — that if we questioned ourselves and dug deeply enough, we would eventually discover that we want what we want (including the body that we want) because we believe that having it will make us happy. This pursuit of happiness is not based on some Freudian reductionist view of a "will to pleasure" based on instincts and drives — it is based on our deepest "hunger." We are hungry for happiness. We are hungry for life. We are hungry for meaning — for peace, for fulfillment, for connection with that which makes us human. And although I use the term happiness in my work, I am referring to the same intrinsic motivation Frankl speaks of in his – the search for meaning.

One of Frankl's most famous quotes – *When the situation cannot be changed, it is we who must change* – directly describes my own story. In *Happy Calories Don't Count* I wrote how – in the face of an untenable, unchangeable situation regarding my body and my weight – I changed. I made a decision – a choice to be happy – and this choice paved the way for healing and transformation. What is significant about this – from a weight loss and body image perspective - is that we are taught that the *situation* can be changed. We are taught (through our mass marketing media driven culture) that because we are responsible for what we eat and what we do for exercise, we *can* lose weight with diet and exercise. We are taught that we *can* get "a body like hers" if we just knew her "secrets" or had enough discipline. We are taught that our bodies *can* be something other than what they are. And it is this underlying belief that the situation can be changed that causes all of our pain and dysfunction around our body, our weight and our self-esteem. When we finally stop trying to change the situation, **we** can change. And when we change, our experience of the situation also changes.

And paradoxically, once our *experience* of the situation changes, the situation itself can often change as well.

To help my clients begin the path of healing and self-transformation, I often advocate a media "diet." (Yes, I am aware of the irony.) In the era of Photoshop, slick marketing, social media, endless cable channels and 24-hour infomercials, it is essential to distance ourselves from any strategic assaults on our self-esteem (at least until we've developed the media and marketing literacy tools to navigate them). Imagine my surprise when I read these words that Viktor Frankl had written in 1947:

> *We are living in an affluent society, and this is an affluence of not only material goods but of various sorts of stimuli as well. We are bombarded by the mass media. We are bombarded by sexual stimuli. And, last but not least, the information explosion represents a further, new affluence. Heaps of books and journals pile up on our desk. Unless we wish to drown... we have to choose between what is important and what is not, what is meaningful and what is not. We have to become selective and discriminating.*

Frankl did not have to deal with the internet and all its glory – the click-bait targeted advertising, the endless sources of information - including legitimate blogs and "fake news." Frankl did not have to deal with social media, streaming videos and podcasts. And his words are truer and more meaningful today than ever before. We must become selective and discriminating about what we choose to let into our personal headspace. We must develop media and marketing literacy skills. And we must take responsibility for ourselves, for our bodies and for our lives. We must take responsibility for our meaning as Frankl would say, and for our happiness as I put it. And we take this responsibility by exercising our freedom of choice. Frankl says it best when he writes:

> *Between stimulus and response, there is a space. In that space lies our freedom and our power to choose our response. In our response lies our growth and our happiness.*

Perhaps my story and the teachings of Happy Calories® really are grounded in an unconscious connection with *Man's Search for Meaning*. Or perhaps the similarity between my work and Frankl's is grounded in our similar struggles for survival. As a holocaust survivor and psychiatrist Frankl often wrote, "See, I have not kept my lips closed." With this book, neither have I.

Chapter 16

Epilogue

My friend is dying
and no one can see

I glance at her every day
smaller
she withers at
every breeze

I never see her smile
only the reflection
of her pale lips
as she shivers
at my warmth

She disappeared today
from my touch to

her own circle
within her family

I know she'll leave soon
on her ship to
an island
where winter is forever.

This poem was written about me, October 24, 1986. I found it while salvaging old boxes in the garage after some winter storm damage. Since Happy Calories Don't Count® is original content based on my own journey of healing and transformation, I shared this poem on my Facebook page. As expected, I received an abundance of "Likes" and positive comments. Of course, I felt grateful – but I was surprised by my internal response to the comments. Many of the remarks expressed gratitude and relief that I made it through "that time" safely. That time, of course, being anorexic. (And those observations were indeed accurate – anorexia has very high death rates.) However, as I read the comments, I felt my inner voice rising up within me screaming, "What? Being anorexic was the *easy* part!"

Now my mother will argue that, "there is nothing

about anorexia that is easy." Of course, she is right. And I am in no way advocating anorexia – or any other eating disorder. I am simply pointing out that in the grand scheme of things, anorexia was relatively easy. It was easy because it fits within the paradigm of the "diet and exercise" culture which says if you want to lose weight, you eat less and move more. Simple. Take it to the extreme and you don't really eat at all. The downside, of course, is that it is not sustainable. You die. Which is a fate to which I came very close – on more than one occasion. But again, it was easy. It was simple. It was clear. I knew what to do. It fit within what we "know" as a society.

Anorexia was easy. Trusting myself despite everything and everyone was very, *very* hard. I was a seventeen-year-old girl who did not have the vocabulary to articulate the concepts I was seeing. The powerful and authoritative medical "experts" were telling me that "it's not about the food" and "it's not about your weight" – but would then focus on the food and my weight. They told me what, when and how much to eat. And every so-called privilege I "earned" was tied to a number on the scale. Anytime I questioned their logic and reasoning their response was "that is your disease talking."

After treatment I was the girl who desperately tried to shed her Scarlet Letter. I was the twenty-something girl who ate "healthy" and worked out. But despite this, I gained weight – a *lot* of it. The personal trainers thought I was "cheating." My doctors told me I had ruined my metabolism by being anorexic. My therapist thought that my attention to my unexplainable weight gain was a sure sign that I was still "sick" – I was too focused on my body and my weight.

I worked like a beast to lose the weight – and felt like after *everything* I was still living an anorexic lifestyle of diets and workouts – still in pain – still fighting with the therapists - but now I was fat too.

It was hard being fat. It was hard feeling like a failure all the time. It was hard hating my body. It was hard hating myself. It was hard falling down the Alice in Wonderland Rabbit Hole of "emotional eating." It was hard navigating the maze of mystical wish fulfillment. It was hard finding a therapist who did not identify me as a label. It was hard being alone. It was hard searching for faith. It was hard to hang on. It was hard to fight for life. *That* was the time that my Facebook friends don't know about. *That* was the time they would really be glad to know that "I got through safely."

But perhaps, the hardest part of all was letting the "eating disorder mentality" go. It was hard to let that go because an "eating disorder mentality" is simply our cultural "diet and exercise" model. Of course, eating disorders are complicated conditions that need professional psychological help. But psychology aside, an eating disorder is simply the following of the "diet and exercise" model a little too well. Even the "experts" at the eating disorder units could not completely untangle "healthy" food and exercise behavior from dysfunctional behavior. And the "diet and exercise" model is embedded within the very fabric of our society. To let that go meant I had absolutely nothing onto which I could hold. And that was hard. That was scary. Choosing that void was the scariest thing I have ever done. That void meant I had to pioneer a new way of being. I had to create a new way of relating to my body and to life. To survive, I had to create Happy Calories Don't Count®. And with that, it is my sincere hope that you don't have it so hard – that whether you deal with a mild case of chronic anxiety about your body or full-on food and weight obsession – your journey is much shorter and much less painful. It is my sincere hope that the principles and steps outlined in this book help you create a sense of peace and freedom around food, exercise and your body.

Your body is the vehicle through which you experience this life. And as such, how you feel in and about your body directly impacts the quality of your life. Lay people often ask me to describe the difference between "Diet Drama Land" and "Happy Calories World." It is an easy enough difference to describe on an intellectual level – feelings of frustration, anxiety, shame, drama etc. around food, exercise, your body and your weight vs. peace, freedom, wellbeing, vitality and joy – and results. But does this accurately and sufficiently describe the experience of freedom – of truly living and enjoying Life – of peace? Some people just won't get it – but there are plenty who do. Here are some words of friends[5] who have already found their way into "Happy Calories World."

This program is changing my whole life! I have been walking around for the past 24 hours totally "in touch" and communicating

---

5   *Only first names are used to maintain privacy.*

with my body and it's completely changing the way I experience every single thing in my life! I feel more freedom than I've ever felt and the guilt and pressure I've always felt around food is little by little, day by day, fading, being replaced by how great I feel in my own skin.

~ Julie Anne

I wanted to thank you and let you know that you have been the final step for me in my journey to freedom from food and weight obsession. It feels like new ground and I feel like a new person.

~ Rachel

I was stuck. I knew from painful years of experience that diets didn't work. And every alternative weight loss approach I tried left me feeling angry, deprived and frustrated. I thought the problem was me. I had a bad attitude, I needed to try harder. Then I came upon Happy Calories Don't Count and had the revelation that the problem wasn't my failure; it was the failure of the diet and exercise model. Carmela's approach is truly revolutionary. She puts forth a new paradigm that not only makes sense, it works. Following her five steps, I appreciate my body, enjoy my food, and made it through the holiday season having lost weight. No need for a New Year's resolution this time.

~ Dana

Changed my life forever. For anyone who has ever struggled, truly and painfully struggled with their body and thought, "What's wrong with me? Why won't it work for me?" The teachings of Carmela Ramaglia will set you free.

~ Ali

You made me look at something that haunted me for life in a way that heals my spirit and psyche. We've all been so conditioned to hate food and/or our bodies. You're like a real-life superhero.

~ Mindy

Epilogue

Carmela is genius at synthesizing all the various modalities of "self-help" and giving us a means to really heal ourselves.

~ Linda

If you had one superpower, what would it be? I am happy to share mine. I *know* you can do this. You *can* be free and be happy. You *can* create a body *and* a life you love.

Appendix

Hungry for More

Living in "Happy Calories World"

It is only with the heart that one can see rightly;
what is essential is invisible to the eye.

~ Antoine de Saint-Exupery

Chapter 17

Frequently Asked Questions

This section was supposed to be "The Top Ten" – the top 10 questions I am most often asked – and their answers. But then I would have to include things like, "What's a Happy Calorie?" (A Happy Calorie has nothing to do with food. It is a concept – a perspective that is explained throughout this entire book and throughout *Happy Calories Don't Count.*) And then I realized I have a lot more than ten frequently asked questions. So here – in no particular order – are the questions I am most often asked and my responses.

What do you eat?

Now most people asking this question have not just read an entire book explaining the principles and steps of Happy Calories Don't Count®. So I hope you understand that I am really not trying to evade the question — but what *I* eat is totally irrelevant. What is important is that *you* connect with *your body* and listen for what your body is asking you to eat. That said — I eat whatever I want whenever I want. I am connected to my body and I trust its impulses. I eat all sorts of things without fear or judgment. I have my preferences, like everyone else. But my preferences are not tied to any sort of "disorder." The only thing that could possibly be argued as a remnant of a "disorder" is the fact that I do not cook — I experience a little PTSD. So what? I take care of myself. I eat things that do not require any cooking, I order take out, and I let my family cook.

What do you do for exercise?

Again, if you paid attention while reading this book you would understand that what I do for exercise is also completely irrelevant. The important thing is that I exercise daily (unless I am sick and my body is requesting some rest). And I exercise in ways I enjoy. And I stay conscious and present with my body through the workout.

Yes, I am a Pilates instructor, so I obviously do Pilates. But I always share that bit of information with some huge caveats. Please do not just read this and think, "Oh Carmela does Pilates, so I'm going to do Pilates." You see, "Pilates" does not really mean anything anymore. Pilates is the name of a man – Joseph Pilates – who created an incredible body of work that has completely transformed my life. However, "pilates" is no longer trademarked. There are no more education, certification or industry standards. The term "pilates" has now become a generic marketing term for "core strength." Moreover, many of the programs claiming to be "Pilates" these days (even if they do use the "reformer" and other specialized apparatus) have little or nothing at all to do with the system of work Joseph Pilates created. In fact, he's probably turning over in his grave! Furthermore, every Pilates instructor is different – with different levels of experience, different goals and different ways of explaining things.

Just because you do "pilates," that does not mean you are doing what I do. So again – you cannot do what I do in terms of "exercise." But you can do what I do in terms of

Happy Exercise® - and that is to do things you enjoy in a way that helps you connect with and inhabit your body. Other things I enjoy for my Happy Exercise® include rebounding, dance aerobic videos in my living room, and hiking.

What if I have a food allergy?

Food allergies are interesting things. How do you know you have a food allergy? Did your body tell you something by reacting to a given food? Did you take some test? During one of the darker periods of my life a naturopath tested me for food allergies – twice. Both times yielded the same result. I was basically allergic to everything. There was nothing I *could* eat. I was literally allergic to food! I find this fascinating in the context of someone who was suffering mightily from food and body drama. Your best bet in dealing with allergies is to talk to your body about them. If you know you have specific allergies, of course – be careful and read labels and such. I am not telling you to be stupid.[6] I am telling you that you can ask your body for guidance, help and support.

Remember, relationships are two-way streets. I had a client who was fearful that she had a gluten allergy.

---

6   *Some allergies can be fatal - shellfish, peanuts, etc. Don't be dumb.*

She was having digestion issues and everyone was telling her it was gluten. She was all stressed out because she had found such freedom and peace and joy in not worrying about her food. She had lost weight too. She was loving "living in Happy Calories World." But then this gluten thing came up and she feared she was going to have to start "watching" what she was eating again. That would be awful!! But she learned that she could ask her body for help. She knew that her body would not give her an impulse to eat something that would make her sick. She was able to let go of the worry and enjoy the food. She realized that she was naturally making more and more gluten-free choices. And then she got tested and found out that she wasn't really allergic to gluten after all.

What if I have injuries or am in pain?

Nothing will make me crabbier faster than hurting. I got very skilled at jumping out of my body when I was anorexic. But now that I work to stay in my body, those injuries, body aches and pain can be extremely frustrating. And again, the answer lies in your body. Only you know what it feels like to be in your body. Only you can sense what is really going on. So as much as it may hurt, take a moment and breathe into it. Explore it – feel it. Let it tell you what it needs to heal. Sometimes it may be rest. Sometimes you need to work through it. Sometimes you might need a massage, chiropractic adjustment or acupuncture treatment. Sometimes you might need ice, heat, or pain-relieving medication.

I understand how frustrating it can be to find a professional practitioner – in any industry – who can truly work with you to reclaim your vibrant wellbeing. Many years ago I injured my ankle. The x-rays showed that it wasn't broken, so I was told to wear a boot and do physical therapy. Well, I never could do those physical therapy exercises successfully no matter how hard I tried. What the x-rays failed to show was that my ankle was partially dislocated. The pain eventually got somewhat better and I continued to walk on it. About ten years after that, my back started going out. The doctor told me I had "degenerative disc disease" and told me there was nothing to do for it. But I would not take that for an answer. So I explored all sorts of alternative healing modalities and started working with a Rolfer for my back issues. She said that my ankle felt "funny" and started working on it. It popped back into place and I can now balance on that side again. And guess what – my crippling back pain has gone. You are the one living in your body. You are the one who knows what feels "right" and feels "off." You are the only one really qualified to take care of your body. Everyone else is just support. So connect with your body and let it tell you how to help it heal.

What if I have an illness?

Those pesky illnesses!! "Illness" is a really broad term, so I am going to focus this discussion on those "mysterious" illnesses that plague us rather than on what to eat if you have the flu. (Ask your body what to eat if you have the flu!) Now if you have been paying attention, I bet you already know what I am going to say: Connect with your body and let it tell you what it wants and needs. This is very important because when we ask "Dr. Google," we can really make ourselves crazy with all of the potential diagnoses and treatments.

There are countless blogs, programs, experts, research studies, etc. that can tell you how to solve your potential problem. So you keep on top of everything and you try something – you see some specialist – and it doesn't work. You try something else – and it doesn't work. You try again – and it doesn't work. And so you get really, really frustrated by all of this effort (and money!) you are putting in and not getting any sort of result. You are up to date with all of the latest information but every time it doesn't work you end up coming back to square one. I do this: Ignore all of the external information. It's simply a different approach.

I stop searching for "the answer." Instead, I breathe and connect with my body. I tune out all of the crazies. I breathe and connect with my body again. Then I go about my day. This issue is something that is indeed important to me – and to my body. So if some bit of information would be relevant to helping me, it will make itself known to me. I will see an article by accident. I will overhear a conversation while waiting in line. A friend will tell me about something they are doing. This thing – whatever came into my experience – is something I could try. It may help – it may not. Either way, I am walking down a path given to me by the energy of Life flowing through me. This "letting the answer come to me" is generally ultimately a more pleasant and effective journey than trying to find a needle in a haystack.

How do I know it's my body and not my head?

When you are skilled at all of this (1. Embracing a Model of Alignment, 2. Connecting with Your Body, 3. Enjoying Your Food, 4. Exercising Daily to Connect With and Tune Your Body and 5. Clearing the Channel) you will not have any stress about this question – you can relax and trust that your body is leading the way. You will not have to worry about your motivations, intentions, that you are somehow unconsciously sabotaging your success or any of those head games. However, this might not happen overnight, right? It is a learning process. So while you are learning, you can ask your body for help! You could say something like, "Hi Body – it's me. I'm trying really hard to learn how to be with you and connect with you, but this is all new. It feels really strange and silly, and I'm probably not very good at it. I'm having this impulse to eat something (or whatever the impulse is). But I can't tell if it's really you or my head talking. Could you please help me out? Could you please give me a really clear, idiot-proof sign – a craving or a strong feeling of distaste or something? I'm going to do my best to hear what you're saying and follow it. But I might screw up. If I do, please forgive me. Please know that I'm trying." See – right there you are putting the question into the context of a relationship with your body. Your body wants to help you out. Your body wants you to be able to help it. Your body will do its best to communicate with you in a way you will understand. Your body will also understand mistakes and your body will forgive you.

What if my body is lying to me?

Why would it? Your body needs you just as much as you need it. It cannot live without you, and everything you do affects it. It is in your body's own best interest to be honest with you.

What about eating for health?

Ah - that "health" thing. Ok, first off you have to understand that Happy Calories® is not a "permission slip" to eat food you think is bad for you or to engage in maladaptive behavior. This is about tuning into the wisdom of your body and following its guidance – which is really hard to do if you think food is "good," "bad," "healthy," or "unhealthy." All of those labels (and corresponding judgment) simply end up being static in the communication channel between you and your body. If you want to "eat for health," then just 1) make sure your thoughts, feelings, beliefs and actions are congruent, 2) you're connected with your body, 3) you enjoy your food, 4) you exercise daily to connect with and tune your body and 5) you clear that channel.

Is it wrong to expect results from exercise?

This question gets tricky because of all the ways it can be interpreted through the "diet and exercise" model and through the wish-fulfillment perspective of the Law of Attraction. So first off – no, it's not "wrong." Nothing is "wrong." Take "wrong" out of your vocabulary. A better thing to focus on is efficacy. Is it effective? The "diet and exercise" model says that your results come from exercise. Is that an effective way to look at things? Is it bringing you peace, happiness and results? The wish-fulfillment perspective of the Law of Attraction would say a couple of contradictory things. Either to expect the results won't bring them because by definition that means you are in a state of lack to begin with and lack will only create more lack – or that you can just manifest results by getting your vibrations to match the vibrational energy of the results you seek. Is any of this effective for helping you find peace, freedom, happiness and results?

In "Happy Calories World" the results do not come directly from the exercise (like the "diet and exercise" model suggests). The results come from Life Force moving through your body when you are in a state of Alignment around the given activity. The results do not come from the specifics of the exercise – the results come from your connection to your body and your connection to yourself around the exercise. It is just a different way of looking at things. For me, personally – and for my clients – this is the happiest and most effective way of looking at things.

What about menopause?

If you are a woman, at some point you are going to go through menopause. Period. You are unique. Your body is unique. Your experience of menopause was, is, or will be unique. And again, even though there are countless opinions on the subject and treatments for the process, I would suggest that you talk to your body about it. I had started to experience some symptoms – sleeplessness, night sweats, hot flashes. And then one day my jeans wouldn't button and I freaked out. "Oh my god! I cannot believe this is happening. My body is freaking out! What am I going to do?" I went to a doctor and she confirmed that I was indeed in the process and had gained the "normal ten pounds." *What?!?* After a few days of freaking out, I finally calmed down and was able to remember all of this stuff that I spend my life teaching other people. I started out by talking to my body and saying how sad and stressed out I was by this weight gain but I understood it needed to do what it needed to do. And if I needed to buy new clothes in a bigger size, so be it. But somewhere along the line I realized that the "conversation" was all about me. It was about *my* stress of gaining weight. It was about *my* hot flashes. It was about *my* discomfort. So I apologized to my body for making it all about me and said that if I was feeling so crappy I couldn't imagine what it was going through. I felt a shift and suddenly all of my anxiety was gone. I told my body I was sorry that it was feeling so out of whack. I asked it what I could do to support it. Nothing unique or special came to mind. So I just continued to connect with my body, listen to it and do what it asked of me. I don't know how long it took – but it seemed to go by really quickly (time flies when you're having fun) – my symptoms are gone and I can button my jeans. Again, this was my unique experience. But it came from my unique connection to my unique body. The best way for you to deal with menopause is for you to connect with your unique body and ask it to help you create your unique plan for dealing with it.

What if I can't exercise like I normally exercise or eat what I normally eat?

I am hoping by now you will already know the answer to this question. Talk to your body about it. Your body is your partner in relationship. Let your body be part of the process. Let it help you. If you cannot do what you normally do – because of illness, travel, or some other unexpected thing – talk to your body about it.

I have had days that were so jammed packed the only way I would be able to get a workout in would be if I were to get up at 4:00 am. Now some people might not have an issue with this. I have PTSD with it. I used to get up at ungodly hours in the middle of the night so I could work out for hours before I had to go to work. My body generally rejects the idea of getting up before 5:00 am (unless I am headed to a film shoot or on a flight to Italy). So when I know those days are coming

I just talk to my body. I say something like, "Tomorrow is going to be one of those days. I'm not going to have time to connect with you in a workout unless we do it at 4:00 am. Do you want to do it? Or do you want to skip it and sleep?" Oftentimes I skip the workout and sleep. But surprisingly, sometimes my body wakes up on its own, bright-eyed and bushy-tailed, ready for a workout.

When it comes to food, you might find yourself at a restaurant and there is absolutely nothing on the menu that you would normally eat. Again, you can ask your body for help. You can say something like, "I seem to have gotten us into a pickle. There isn't really anything here that I think you'd like. Can you help me out? Let's look at the menu together and when we find something that would be the best (or least offensive) option would you let me know? Please forgive me. I promise I'll do better next time." And your body will happily help you navigate that. Remember – it is in your body's best interest to help you help it!

What if I make a mistake and "emotionally eat" or overeat?

All eating is emotional eating – being hungry does not feel good. In "Happy Calories World," emotional eating is a good thing because your body always tells you when, what and how much to eat. If the question is about a "mistake" about eating to try to not feel bad or about overeating to the point of a tummy ache, I hope by now you know what I am going to say. What would you do if you "made a mistake" in any other relationship? Talk to your body about it. Ask your body for forgiveness. You do not need to punish yourself. (You can't "burn it off" with exercise or "balance it out" by skipping meals anyway.) That tummy ache is "punishment" enough. It is your body's way of expressing its displeasure. Tell your body that you are sorry and do your best to let it go.

What's your take on 12-Step Programs?

Twelve-step programs can be really great resources for people. I don't think I would have survived grad school without my daily AA meeting. Nope, not an alcoholic. But I was alone. I desperately needed support and an open AA meeting was my only option. It turned out to be a really great option. I basically kept my mouth shut and listened. The people in those meetings talked about "real stuff" and offered me genuine support. But 12-Step programs do not work for everyone and they become especially tricky when you are dealing with an issue that cannot simply be cut out of your life – like food. I thrived in AA, but when my schedule changed my only option was OA (Overeaters Anonymous). And that was a disaster. It was a disaster because they were trying to work the 12-Steps (of a program created for a substance that can indeed be completely eliminated from your life) from within the context of the diet and exercise model. So just as with everything else, the 12-Steps of OA never truly solve the real underlying core issue. Try the 12-Steps from within the relationship-based framework of Happy Calories Don't Count® and I am sure they'll work great. But then again, we only need five steps.

What should I do if I'm craving sugar or ice cream, but I don't think it's good for me? What if listening to my body is "out of alignment?"

I love this question!! This is a perfect example of how you can let your body help you and let your thoughts and beliefs evolve. When you are first discovering "Happy Calories World," remember that baby steps are ok. You won't be "perfect" because there is no such thing – you are "in relationship." So talk to your body about it. Tell your body that you are having strong feelings to eat something but that your head does not think that thing is good for you. Tell it that you trust it – or that you are trying really hard to learn to trust it. Tell your body that you know – or are trying to know – that it would not give you an impulse to eat something that would harm you in any way. Ask it for help.

Depending on how strong your negative thoughts and beliefs are about this food, you could ask your body for different things. If you really have strong negative beliefs, you could ask your body to soften your craving for whatever that thing is. You could ask your body to come up with some other type of food that would still give your body the essence of what it desires – but in a food that you are much more comfortable eating. If your negative beliefs about that food are not extreme – just negative enough to give you a bit of anxiety about it – you could tell your mind that you are going to "do an experiment" with trusting your body. That could soften some of those negative thoughts and beliefs.

Interestingly, I – and many of my clients – have had the experience of having a really strong craving for some food that traditionally came with strong negative beliefs about gaining weight. After wrestling with the anxious thoughts and finally deciding to "trust our body" and eat whatever – the craving disappeared. I often wonder if that is one of our body's ways of discovering if it can trust us. Remember, oftentimes our relationship with our body is abusive – and *we* are the abuser. Perhaps our body needs to learn that it can trust us as much as we need to learn that we can trust it.

My body is the furthest thing from "optimized." What do you recommend for people with special needs?

Ok, first you need to understand that to "optimize" your body does not mean that you will suddenly become a 6'3" supermodel – or whatever the current standard of health or beauty happens to be. Optimize means just that – optimize – to make as efficient, effective, functional, vibrant, and awesome as possible. And you can do that right now. It does not matter if you are over or under weight. It does not matter if you are in a wheelchair. It does not matter if you have a serious illness. Of course these things matter, because they affect you. But in terms of "optimizing," all of that is irrelevant. Whatever your physical, mental, emotional, spiritual condition is right now – you can take steps right now to optimize yourself in this moment. For example, if you are one hundred pounds heavier than you would like to be, "optimization" does not come when you have lost that hundred pounds. You can create a state of harmony and congruency with yourself right now. Right now – at this weight – you can allow that Life Force energy flow powerfully through your Aligned Self to become "optimized." And in the next moment, you use all the skills and tools you have and everything you have learned in this book to recreate an optimized state. And in the next moment, you do it again. The same is true if you have an illness. And even if you are in a wheelchair and will always be wheelchair bound, your body can be in a state of optimization within its physical limitations.

Optimization comes from reconciling your thoughts, feelings, beliefs and actions so that you can be congruent with yourself. Optimization is about letting Life Force flow efficiently, effectively and powerfully through you on your behalf. Optimization is creating that state in which you are connected with Life Energy so that you can be happy and shine – regardless of where you are on your personal journey.

Help! My body isn't listening to me! What do I do?

This is always an interesting one. How do you know your body is not listening to you? Because it is not giving you what you want? Because it is not changing as quickly as you want it to? Relationships are two-way streets. They are built on respect and communication. Are you listening to your body? How do you know you are listening to your body and not just talking at it? Are you really connecting with your body? I do not ask this question lightly – or with any sort of derision. I am the Queen of Thinking Instead of Doing. I speak or write about these principles all day long, so I am constantly thinking about being in my body and constantly thinking about talking to my body. And since I am constantly thinking about it, I can think that I am actually doing it when I'm really not. You know how oftentimes we casually use this concept called "god." We will be in a conversation and say something like, "God, I hope not!" or "God help me!" And then we might have times in our lives that literally bring us to our knees. And we might not even know if we really believe if there is anything out there or not, but we are humbled and we are begging for help. "Dear God, please help." These are two very different ways of interacting with this thing called "god." They have very different qualities. So before you start freaking out and jumping to conclusions about how your body isn't listening to you (because it is not doing what you want it to do), check in and see if you are really present and creating an honest-to-goodness dialogue and relationship with your body.

What is your guilty pleasure?

HA! This question is usually asked during media interviews or panel discussions by a person who has not had the time (energy, interest, motivation) to learn about Happy Calories®. Otherwise they would know that "guilty" is not congruent with "pleasure," and thus I have no guilty pleasures. I have plenty of guilt – my good Italian Catholic genes demand that. And I have plenty of pleasures. But I have no guilty pleasures – particularly when it comes to food.

What is your favorite food and dessert?

Again, I am not trying to be evasive. But these questions – and their answers – change within the context of the Happy Calories Don't Count® framework. My "favorite" food and dessert will be whatever my body wants in the moment. Something can't really be a "favorite" if it doesn't taste good – and if my body is not "in the mood" for it, it won't want it and it will only taste, "Meh." In the context of how this question is traditionally asked, I would normally answer that my favorite food is Authentic Neapolitan Pizza Margherita – signed off on by the pizza police – aka VPN. (Yes, Neapolitans are passionate about their pizza and there is such a thing as the pizza police! You can check out Associazione Verace Pizza Napoletana.) But last time I was in Italy, I was over it in two days. My body had had enough. We have a really good local pizzeria (pizza police approved), but I don't always ask to go there on Date Night. Sometimes I want Mexican food. And on those nights, that is my favorite. It is the same answer for desserts – whatever my body wants is my "favorite" that moment. That pizza police approved place has an incredible Nutella Calzone dessert filled with blackberries and raspberries. But I only want it every now and again. And there have been times when my sweetie brought home my "favorite" Dryers Drumstick Ice Cream, only to have it sit in the freezer for 3 weeks before I was inspired to have some. So my "favorite" anything really does depend on what my body wants in the moment. I know this question was about food, but it is the same for exercise. I love Pilates, but some days I would rather hike or dance around my living room. It is all about connecting with the body and letting it be our guide.

What if I don't know what my body wants to eat (or do for exercise)?

Most people tend to routinely eat the same general types of things. So, when you don't know what your body is asking you to eat, try this process. Take a deep breath and drop into your body as best as you can. Then imagine eating something that you'd normally eat. Imagine eating something else. Then imagine a third and perhaps forth option. When you hit that thing your body wants, it will tell you. Generally, you will feel some sort of shift. The anxiety from not knowing what to eat disappears. You will feel a pull or a sense of calm. That is your body telling you what it wants. If you don't feel that with any of the traditional things you normally eat, let your mind imagine other foods and see how your body responds. I hear reports of people experiencing revulsion when bringing to mind a food – a clear sign that their body does not want to eat what they just imagined. They also experience a "meh" for a give or take. And they just "know" – it just "feels right" when they hit the thing their body wants.

And if this little exercise doesn't do the trick, you know what I am going to say. Ask your body for help. Tell it that you are having trouble figuring out what it wants to eat and ask it to help you hear it better. The same process can be done for exercise. Imagine doing various physical activities and feel how your body responds. Your body is always communicating with you. And it is in your body's best interest to help you help it. Your actions literally affect your body, so it will do its very best to work with you.

I eat healthy. I just like my wine and I'm not giving it up.

This is not really a question, but I hear it a lot more than I would have expected. (In fact, I did not expect this to come up at all.) Also, this statement is often said with short, curt, defensiveness. So, first off, I am not a medical doctor, psychiatrist, psychologist or any of that and I would never presume to diagnose anyone with anything. Furthermore, I am not making any statements that condone maladaptive, dysfunctional behaviors that keep you in a state of being less than your best self. That said, from a Happy Calories® perspective, it feels to me like the women who make these types of statements are still operating from within the context of the "diet and exercise" model. In that model, you can "drink your calories" as well as eat them. So to me, it often feels like these women talk about their wine with such resolve because they think (consciously or unconsciously) that the calories in the wine they drink are responsible for the extra weight – or whatever it is about their bodies that they do not like. And they are in conflict with that because they do not want to give up the wine (like they may have given up various foods) – so they are a bit defiant. But in the Happy Calories Don't Count® model, the wine itself has no direct effect on your weight – we are not thinking in terms of transaction-based "diet and exercise." We think in terms of relationship-based Alignment. So, from a Happy Calories® perspective, any "extra" weight could be from being in conflict about thinking they need to give up the wine calories but not being willing to sacrifice the pleasures of drinking wine. For that conflict creates disharmony – the system of thoughts, feelings, beliefs and actions becomes misaligned and Life Energy cannot flow freely. It is not about the wine. It is about your body. The wine is simply a vehicle through which you express yourself in relationship with your body. Connect with your body and it will tell you what to do. And if you are one of the many women who drinks her nightly glass of red wine to unwind because the Terrible Twos have turned your toddler into a tyrant or because of the political subterfuge of the PTA or because of something stressing you out at work, simply ask yourself if you are drinking to feel better or if you are drinking to not feel bad. Drinking to not feel bad will never work because we can never not feel.

You don't understand my life. I'm a mother of three, I work full time, and I'm in graduate school. I don't have time to sleep, let alone exercise.

I understand that life can be chaotic and overwhelming and I'm not here to shame you by questioning your "commitment to your goals" or "priorities." All I am saying is that your body is one more relationship in your busy life. You can negotiate with it and ask it for support. You love all of your children equally – and they each have a unique relationship with you. They are all different ages (unless they are twins or triplets), engaged in life differently and demand different things from you in terms of time and attention. Your boss and work colleagues have relationships with you – as do your professors and fellow students. You negotiate all of these relationships already – just add your body to the mix by acknowledging it. You could say something like, "I'm sorry that I have ignored you. This is the first I'm learning about having a relationship with you. Life is really chaotic right now. My days are really full and I'm flying through life by the seat of my pants. Could you please help me? I'm going to practice taking moments here and there to breathe into you. Can you please inspire me toward food choices that will give us the most energy? I'm also sorry that I can't dedicate a full hour every day to a workout date with you. But I can practice connecting with you in small increments throughout the day. We can take mini stretch breaks and you can tell me how you want me to move to help support you. This schedule won't last forever. I'll be done with school and my children are growing. I promise to include you in my most important relationships. I'll connect with you more and ask for your guidance more. And please understand my current situation. If you can help give me energy to get through these long days, I promise I'll make it up to you somehow – a hiking trip, a spa day, whatever you want." When you view your body as your partner in relationship, you have a completely different approach to solving problems and overcoming challenges.

Chapter 18

Tasty Treats

One of my friends has a "Can't Cope Box." I don't know if it is an actual box or not, but it is the idea that this is where he puts things when he doesn't know where else to put them and "can't cope." In a sense, this is sort of a "can't cope" chapter – designed to help you cope! It is simply a bunch of "Carmela-isms" – things I find myself saying all the time to my clients or things I post to social media. Some of these "treats" are definitely petit four bite size while other passages are longer. Again, my former English professors would criticize me for the redundancy of ideas. But after years of teaching, I have learned that oftentimes saying the exact same thing in just a slightly different way is the key that will help someone have an "Aha" moment. I hope in moments of stress, panic or anxiety, you can pull out these nuggets and they will help you cope. Without further ado, and in no particular order, here we go:

Acceptance is not giving up wanting what you want. Acceptance is giving up the pain around not having what you want in this particular moment.

Acceptance is not resignation – it is the key to freedom.

All eating is emotional because being hungry doesn't feel good.

It is about the food until it's not – the way to make it "not about the food" is to make it about your body.

"Self-control" does nothing to control your body.

You will always lose a battle with your body – befriend it and you will create a win-win.

Anxiety around your body is a sign that you are disconnected from it.

No one else knows what it is like to be you. No one else knows what it's like to be in your body. Trust yourself. Trust your body.

Stop doing all of the millions of little things that make you feel bad about yourself.

You don't need to love yourself – just stop hating yourself.

There is no relationship between diet and exercise – the relationship is between you and your body.

You are going to be with your body for the rest of your life, so it will only serve you to develop a relationship with it.

Blame does not create empowerment.

Personal transformation is not a sound bite.

You can have all the "self-control" in the world and it still won't help you control your body.

Your body knows how to create an optimized state of health, vitality and beauty and is always guiding you in that direction.

Your body has your best interests at heart.

Your body has an intelligence and wisdom of its own.

Your body always knows what, when, and how much to eat.

Your body is not the enemy — in fact it is your greatest ally.

Your body has its own point of view.

The journey is the destination.

Comparing yourself to others will disconnect you from

your body faster than you can say, "diet drama."

Comparing yourself to others is one of the most insidious and body-shaming behaviors you can engage in – stop it!

The comparison game is just a habit – maybe unconscious – but still a habit. And habits can be broken.

Despite all of your abuse – the dieting, the starving, the bingeing, the body-bashing workouts, the lack of movement, the shaming and the blaming – your body is still here for you. Take a moment to acknowledge that and thank it.

When you're having a tough time remember that diamonds are born of pressure and heat. Hold on, breathe and know that this experience is transforming you. You will soon sparkle and shine.

Dieting is disrespectful to your body.

There is a difference between thinking about connecting with your body and actually connecting with your body.

You will never be completely free of your weight and body issues as long as you continue to view your body as a result of what and how much you eat (or don't) and how much you exercise (or don't).

You create your reality, but you cannot control your reality.

Every time you judge your food as good or bad - you judge yourself too.

Faking it will not help you make it.

What can you do right now to feel better?

Feeling better is its own reward – feeling better feels better than feeling bad.

Feeling good about your body matters.

Feeling good in your body matters.

Your body is the vehicle through which you experience this life.

How you feel in and about your body directly impacts the quality of your life.

Your dog doesn't care what size it is, and it still wants to go for a walk every day.

Exercise has absolutely nothing at all to do with burning calories or losing weight.

Exercise is not a penalty.

Exercise is not a punishment.

Exercise is not the price you have to pay to eat!

Food cannot be earned.

Food is not the enemy – food is not your friend – food is just food.

Food Is Not a Four-Letter Word

Food is not a four-letter word.

Food is not a four-letter word – but diet is! ☺

A self-made prison is still a prison.

Eating to feel better will always work. It's the eating to not feel bad that never works.

Eating to not feel bad will never work because we can never not feel.

You cannot compel yourself to love anything, let alone your body.

That's the fallacy. The idea that we can control the outcome. That's the hook in our hearts that keeps us in pain.

Every mirror is a magic mirror.

Mirrors are magical because they do not reflect reality – they reflect our state of being.

That magic mirror will always give us what we seek.

Let your body be your best friend.

Respect your body and communicate with it.

Trust your body and teach it that it can trust you.

Judgment creates pain. Judgment comes back to bite you.

You cannot judge others without also judging yourself.

Becoming embodied truly is the key to healing everything.

You are the only one really qualified to take care of your body.

You are completely and totally unique – there is no comparison.

You are enough.

Stop sizing yourself up.

Stop sizing others up.

When you look in the mirror, what are you really looking for?

You can't not be beautiful.

You can't not have worth.

You can't not be enough.

You have the energy of Life running through you – you can't not be beautiful, have worth, or be enough.

Happy Calories® is not a "permission slip" to eat food you think is bad for you or to engage in maladaptive behavior. Happy Calories gives you permission to connect with your body.

Heal your relationship with your body and everything else falls into place.

If you don't take care of your body, who will?

Your body is always talking to you — are you listening?

Are you listening to respond or to understand?

Act from inspiration not desperation.

Your body has your back.

You will never "win" the battle of the bulge. By definition this idea keeps you in a state of constant war with your body (either active combat or a cold war). It makes your body the enemy and keeps you in pain.

When you truly get that there is no one to compare yourself to, you will start to see your own brilliance and your own beauty.

Your past may inform your present, but it does not need to define your future.

Your greatest power is choice. You cannot control what Life brings you, but you have the power to choose how you interpret Life situations, the power to choose how you will engage with them and the power to choose how you will experience them.

Pay attention to your body – what is it saying to you?

Real life has wrinkles.

When an orchid and rose are side by side – is one more beautiful than the other?

There is no wagon.

If you have struggled with the body shame and low self-esteem that comes along with "diet drama," you are intimately aware of the emotional hits you take when you believe that you've "fallen off the wagon." So to rewrite a line from The Matrix: Do not try to stay on the wagon for that is impossible. Instead, only try to realize the truth. There is no wagon. Then you'll see that it is not the wagon you stay on, but yourself.

By its very nature transformation demands that you release yourself into the process.

Transformation takes courage. You must give up what you have always thought and believed to become who you can truly be.

Trust your body.

What is your body asking of you?

Work with your body – not against it.

You are not your body – you are in a relationship with your body.

Your body has no idea what a calorie is.

Your body is not the enemy.

Your body is your GPS.

Your body loves you.

Your body needs you.

Breathe.

Be here now.

Your body is constantly changing – every moment of every day.

Photographs are not reality; they are works of art.

You don't need to be a better you – you just need to allow you to be.

You don't need to worry about loving your body. Your body already loves you and that's enough for now.

Every time you judge your food as "good" or "bad" you are judging yourself as well. Stop the self-judgment and the shame by ceasing to judge your food. Food isn't good or bad - it's just food. (And what you eat doesn't make you "good" or "bad" either). It's how we RELATE to food (and exercise, and our bodies, and ourselves) that can be dysfunctional. Heal your relationship with your body and everything else falls into place.

Your body is a complex system of living intelligence. It knows how to create an optimized state of health, vitality, wellbeing and joy - and it is always guiding you in that direction.

While self-love and body positivity are noble and worthwhile goals, it's impossible to "just love yourself." All of that noise out there shouting "Love your body! Rock your curves! Love yourself!" is just that - noise. And it's another layer of social pressure to work through. Love cannot be compelled. You can't simply "love yourself" or your body no matter how hard you try. What you CAN do, however, is stop hating yourself. You can stop doing all of those millions of little things you unconsciously do all day long that undermine your self-esteem. When you stop engaging in all of the negative, self-loathing habits, you create a space where Love can authentically bloom.

Your body is not the enemy - in fact, it is your greatest ally. You need your body and your body needs you. You two are in this Life together. The best way to create happiness and success for you both is to work together.

Your body has a wisdom and intelligence all its own. It can cure itself of illness and heal itself of wounds. It can even create and sustain Life itself. Your body knows how to create an optimized state of health, vitality and beauty and is always communicating with you to achieve this goal. But it is very hard to hear the messages coming forth from your body if you are 1) constantly criticizing and shaming it or 2) continually trying to "wish it" into a new form. Stop all of that and just connect and listen to the impulses coming forth. Then follow that guidance the best you can (regardless of what external opinions may have to say).

You are the only one really qualified to take care of your body and yourself. You are the one inhabiting your body, so you are the one it speaks to. You are the one in a position to hear what it wants and needs and to take action on its behalf. You are the only one who really knows what you truly think and feel and believe. So you are the only one who can create alignment within yourself. You are the only one experiencing your life. You must take care of yourself - there's no one else...

Food is not your enemy. Food is not your friend. Food is just food. The relationship is between you and your body and food is a vehicle through which you express that relationship. Heal the relationship with your body and all of your "issues" around food are also healed.

In the era of Photoshop, slick imagery and social media, it's important to remember that real life has wrinkles! Our faces get wrinkles when we laugh - and when we cry. Our clothes get wrinkles from sitting, moving, and wearing them. Our lives are full of wrinkles - happy and sad. We see a beautiful sunset, hear a song or fall in love. We suffer loss and heartache. Our feelings are important - they make us human. But don't ever let yourself feel bad about having wrinkles in your life.

Comparing yourself to others - or even to past versions of yourself - is one of the most insidious body-shaming behaviors you can engage in. Sometimes this behavior is conscious, sometimes it isn't. But you'll always know when you are doing it because you become anxious and start to experience "diet drama" or "body drama." Calm the anxiety by dropping into your body and then stop comparing yourself - and judging yourself - to others.

Feeling better is its own reward. There are many in the metaphysical community who teach that feeling better is the key to "manifesting" your dream body. But when you approach it from that perspective, your feelings are always tied to a physical end result (what you see in the mirror). And if the results aren't apparent, it influences the way you feel (usually in a negative way). You want to feel better simply because feeling better feels better than feeling bad! Life is too long to feel bad! Furthermore, you only wanted to create the body you want in the first place because you thought having it would make you feel better. Feeling better is the gift you're truly searching for - it is its own reward.

You cannot "earn" your food and you cannot "burn it off." Food is food and exercise is exercise. They are completely independent of one another. They are both ways in which you express yourself in relationship to your body - but they are not related to each other.

You don't need to "start on Monday." That kind of thinking implies that you have to prepare yourself to follow some program outside of yourself (because doing that is hard – and oftentimes incongruent - work). You don't need to "prepare" yourself because you're not giving anything up – you're not doing anything you don't want to do. All you're doing is connecting with your body and letting it guide you to a state of health, vitality, freedom, peace and joy. And you can start doing that in any moment you choose.

Transformation takes courage. It isn't always easy to change a thought or belief. It's not a simple matter of "wishing" or "deciding" a new way of thinking and believing. A belief cannot be compelled. Thoughts and beliefs change as a result of experiences you encounter in Life and the willingness to let yourself be transformed.

Your body is your innate guidance system. It will guide

you to where you want to go - but you must connect with it and follow its guidance.

Your body needs you as much as you need it. It's in your body's best interest to have your best interest at heart. Relax and trust your body. Follow its guidance.

Your body is the one constant in your life. It's been with you on this journey the entire time. Wouldn't it make sense to heal your relationship with it? Try this perspective and see how your life - and body – transform.

Chapter 19

One Last Bite

Before I go, I would like to share with you an email (edited for length) I received from a former client. Dana has not only given me explicit permission to share it, she was eager for you to hear (and perhaps learn from) her experience.

Dear Carmela,
I hope this email finds you happy in every
sense of the word. I am writing to give you
a brief summary of what has transpired for
me with regards to my weight and my rela-

tionship with my body over the past several years. In part, this is a thank you for getting me started on this path, and in addition, my experience may be helpful to others.

As you know, I worked with you many years ago in a weekly program to learn about Happy Calories Don't Count. The biggest take away from our work together was about entering a new relationship with my body. I still remember some of the exercises we did! While I didn't lose much weight, I stopped gaining weight, my binge eating greatly diminished, and I truly started listening to my body and working together as a "co-creative" team.

Then, one morning, out of the blue, as I was taking my daily medication for heartburn, I got this very strong message that I needed to stop taking this medication. I had known for some time that one of its major side effects is osteoporosis in post-menopausal women (that's me). ...I had tried a couple of times in the past (to go off the medication) and was unsuccessful. But this feeling from my body could not be ignored and after some research, I chose a program and worked with the man who had developed this approach to stopping heartburn by making lifestyle changes, which included food intake.

While this lifestyle change was pretty dramatic, I had NO problems following the protocol. I continued on the program and eventually made it my own, eating in a way that I could easily live with moving forward. I continued to lose weight.

Now for the most surprising twist.

As I lost weight, and more and more people noticed and complimented me on my weight loss, I began to get totally caught up in the diet mentality. I was not aware that I had stopped nurturing my relationship with my body. Now I was totally focused on how much I weighed, giving myself new "numbers" on the scale as a goal, wanting to get down to the next smaller size. I began to eat larger quantities of food to see "what I could get away with" in terms of not gaining weight and then when I would overeat, I would berate myself. OMG, those old feelings from the diet mentality of self-loathing were resurfacing and I felt just as bad at this weight as I had before I lost weight. What was going on??

Then I remembered: I needed to get back in connection with my body. I have been working on that and feel like my body and I are friends again. But I am humbled and shocked by how easy it was to lose my way, to get caught up in the diet mentality.

After receiving your email this morning, I was motivated to write... and tell you how much I appreciate your message. Weight loss is not about diet and exercise. It starts with my relationship with my body. We are back communicating (my body and me) and our journey together is once again one of peace and harmony.

Much appreciation and best wishes,
Dana

The 5 Steps of the Happy Calories Don't Count® Method are very simple. But simple does not necessarily mean easy — especially in the culture in which we live. If you ever feel lost or like you want or need support, please don't hesitate to reach out. You are not alone. I am here for you (as are all the other great people in "Happy Calories World"). You can reach me via my website at www.CarmelaRamaglia.com. And since I didn't want you to worry about having to know how to spell my name, you can always find me at www.HappyCalories.com too. You can also find me via social media. Platforms may change with popularity or technology. Instagram[7] has replaced Facebook[8] as "the place to be" and they could both go the way of MySpace and be replaced by something completely new by the time you read this. So, whatever the platform is, look for me with a handle like "HappyCaloriesDontCount" or "HappyCalories." (These phrases are trademarked so you should be able to be sure you are finding me.)

You *can* do this. I *know* you can. You *can* create happiness **and** a body that you love. Be well and be happy!

---

7   *Instagram.com/happy.calories.dont.count*
8   *Facebook.com/HappyCaloriesDontCount*

About the Author

Carmela's last name isn't nearly as scary as it looks. Ramaglia (rah-MAHL-ya). The "g" is silent. It's Italian. She earned her Ph.D. in personal transformation with an emphasis in body image, self-esteem and weight loss from the very prestigious School of Hard Knocks. Her signature Model of Alignment and 5-Step "Happy Calories Don't Count" Method have helped women from all across the world find freedom from food drama and body shame while also optimizing physical results. A

Classically trained Certified Pilates Instructor, Carmela continues to see private clients in her boutique studio, as well as guest teach around the country. She appreciates how teaching Pilates grounds and connects her while dovetailing with "Happy Calories" in a deep and meaningful way. Carmela is also an actress and commercial print model. She has heard in more than one check-out line, "Did I see you on TV?" When not working, Carmela can be found rocking out to '80s Hair Bands, loving on her fur babies, and hanging out with her family. She can be reached at www.CarmelaRamaglia.com